MY FATHER'S LIFE

RÉTIF DE LA BRETONNE
MY FATHER'S LIFE

Translated with an Introduction by Richard Veasey
School of European Studies, University of Sussex

ALAN SUTTON
1986

Alan Sutton Publishing Limited
30 Brunswick Road
Gloucester GL1 1JJ

First published in translation 1986

British Library Cataloguing in Publication Data

Rétif de la Bretonne
 My father's life.
 I. Title   II. La vie de mon père. *English*
 843'.5[F]   PQ2025.V6

 ISBN 0-86299-176-5

Cover picture: detail from Poor Fauvette *by
Bastien Lepage.
Glasgow Museum and Art Gallery.*

Typesetting and origination by
Alan Sutton Publishing Limited.
Photoset Bembo 9/10.
Printed in Great Britain
by The Guernsey Press Company Limited,
Guernsey, Channel Islands.

CONTENTS

Introduction   vii

My Father's Life   1

    Book 1   3

    Book 2   41

    Book 3   77

    Book 4   103

The Ploughman's Wife   145

INTRODUCTION

Nicolas-Edme Rétif de la Bretonne was not, as one might suppose, of noble birth, though he liked to pretend half jokingly that he was descended from the Roman Emperor Pertinax on his father's side and that his mother was one of the de Bertro family of Accolai. Born on 23rd October, 1734 at Sacy, twelve or so miles south-east of Auxerre in Burgundy, he was in fact the son of a hard-working and well-to-do peasant farmer. His father had recently married the lively thirty-one year old Barbe Ferlet (his second wife), nearly thirteen years his junior. There were seven surviving children of Edme's first marriage, the eldest of whom was twenty; and another eight were to be born to Barbe in the next ten years, two of whom died in infancy. In 1740, Edme acquired the house and land known as La Bretonne, situated at the other end of the village, and the family moved there when Rétif was eight. If we are to believe Rétif, Edme came to own land worth 50,000 francs, some £2,000 in English money of the time, whereas an ordinary holding in the area might have been worth 720 francs or £30. Edme's undoubtedly superior position in economic terms was further enhanced by his status in the community as village notary and justice of the peace. As a result, and because he was better dressed than most other children, his son was addressed as 'Monsieur' Nicolas. Though there was some dissension between his mother and her elder stepdaughters, Rétif was born into a loving and protective family, which gave him a strong sense of security to which he harked back with growing nostalgia the older he got.

In his autobiography, *Monsieur Nicolas*, the first three volumes of which were published in 1794, Rétif refers to his passionate and sensitive nature as a child, describing how he fainted when tickled by one of his sisters and how he was fearful of men, of dogs, of the sight of blood and even of caterpillars. From a tender age he showed a marked predilection for the opposite sex and later boasted of his sexual precocity. 'I was handsome,' he writes, 'my golden-chestnut hair was curly, giving me the appearance of those angels, children of the smiling imagination of Italian painters.' Though he enjoyed being admired by pretty young girls, his cherubic and somewhat effeminate features seemed to invite their kisses, which only served to intensify his shyness and his humiliation in the eyes of the other boys who teased him. But when he was nearly twelve, he contracted smallpox and suddenly became ugly. 'The first time I saw myself in the mirror, it was with a kind of horror.' Rétif is not, however, simply lamenting his lost good looks; he is expressing an awareness of ugliness which has strong moral overtones.

Nonetheless, Sacy was for him 'the earthly paradise'; and nowhere is this more evocatively and powerfully expressed than in the descriptions of the days he spent guarding his father's sheep and goats as they grazed, whilst he ate blackberries and sweet wild pears. As a shepherd-boy he was at last like the children of other peasants. Yet when he wandered one day into an isolated valley, it was transformed in his imagination into his own little kingdom. He built a monument of a pile of stones on which he created a rudimentary altar. Then he sacrificed a bird of prey, with his friends gathered round him as his congregation. At the same time, he roasted a skylark and shared it amongst them in a quasi-religious feast. In nature and especially when alone, Rétif enjoyed a feeling of independence and of freedom which made him value greatly his life as a country boy. Indeed, at times his strongest wish was to follow in his father's footsteps and remain on the land. But not all his pleasures were as idyllic as the days he spent shepherding the animals. Several of the games the village children played – with names such as 'wolf', 'maiden', 'step-mother' – were often rough and sometimes even indecent. There was also the less than wholesome influence of certain farmhands his father employed. François and Pierre Courtcou were particularly crude, and their conversation full of obscenities according to Rétif. They told the young Nicolas frightening and salacious stories about devils, witches and beautiful young girls; and on one occasion Pierre involved him in a ceremony in which he tried to summon up the devil.

Stories were an important part of Rétif's childhood. On winter evenings, his father read to them not only the books of the Old Testament but tales of ghosts and robbers as well from the French equivalent of chapbooks, the popular stories sold by pedlars. Rétif also began to read at an early age, mostly religious works at first such as a Life of Christ, the Psalter, and several books of the Old Testament which he could soon recite by heart. In consultation with his cousin, lawyer Jean Rétif of Noyers, Edme therefore decided that his son was too intelligent to spend the rest of his days as a peasant. So, at the age of twelve, Rétif was sent to Bicêtre near Paris where his elder brother, the abbé Thomas, was in charge of the choirboys. It was also a way of removing him from the pernicious influence of uncouth country lads, his father felt. Thomas's marked hostility to his young step-brother together with the austere and ordered life and the stern morality of Bicêtre made the year he spent there an uncomfortable one. Yet though he disliked the narrow-minded dogmatism of the Jansenists, he recognized that their teaching encouraged sustained reflection and self-examination, exercising and strengthening the mind, and for this he was grateful. As an adult, Rétif was to claim that he had developed a more 'enlightened' moral code, but Jansenist teaching certainly left its mark on him. His sense of fatality, so often expressed in terms of damnation, and his constant preoccupation with his moral laxity bear this out.

When the new Archbishop of Paris initiated a campaign against the Jansenists, Thomas and Nicolas joined their elder brother Nicolas-Edme who was the parish priest of Courgis, near Chablis in Burgundy. There Rétif continued his education, learning Latin and Greek, with the intention of entering the Church in his turn. It was at Courgis, however, that there occurred one of the most significant events of his life. On Easter Day, 1748, when he was just thirteen and a half, Rétif saw for the first time and fell hopelessly in love with the modest and lovely Jeannette Rousseau. She was the incarnation of an ideal, someone to whom he never spoke; but she inspired him to work hard at his studies, to purify his heart and his thoughts so that one day he might be worthy of her. He was obsessed; gazing at her in church, kissing the spot where she knelt, and looking up and memorizing her date of birth and of baptism in the parish register. Jeannette was for him a divinity whom he idolized. Rétif was, however, on the verge of puberty and beginning to experience sexual desires which threatened to overwhelm him. These he began to exorcize by fantasizing about them in writing. Having secretly borrowed his brother's copy of the plays of Terence, he started to write a rather obscene play of his own. Then he tried his hand at poetry, modelled on amatory verses he managed to acquire. In the most extraordinary of the poems which he claims to have written, he imagines himself rewarded by the king for valiant deeds with the gift of an enclosure of land together with a house in which he would live with the twelve girls of his choice. Unfortunately for Rétif, his exercise book was found and his father summoned from Sacy to be presented with the evidence of his son's corruption. Thereafter, all books were removed and his education terminated by his increasingly unsympathetic brothers. It was only a matter of months before he returned to Sacy.

In the early hours of 14th July, 1751, Rétif set out on a journey which was to be a decisive turning-point in his life. He was not quite seventeen. Having visited many friends and relatives in the preceding days to bid them farewell and receive their good wishes, and having been bought new clothes by his mother – a brown suit, rough silk stockings, a hat and town shoes – he was ready to embark on his apprenticeship as a printer in Auxerre. With his father's prayers and blessing for a virtuous and prosperous life, Rétif thus achieved his independence. Once installed at François Fournier's, he quickly discovered that he was the lowest of the low. His earliest tasks included picking up and sorting the characters which had fallen to the floor, sweeping up the shop, and running errands for the other workers. Because he could read and write, some of them also expected him to write and then deliver billet-doux to their girlfriends. They played jokes on him too; sending him off on one occasion to the locksmith's to be measured for his 'iron gloves', whence he returned with a band riveted to his wrist.

But Rétif's earlier education had not been wasted. He worked hard, learned quickly, and neither drank nor gambled like the others. Furthermore, he developed his literary taste as he began to read more widely: the novels of Mme de Villedieu (a popular seventeenth-century novelist), the fables of La Fontaine, and the plays of Corneille, Molière and above all Racine. And though he was still writing verses as a way of relieving his passion for the various girls he saw or met, he was also beginning to record the principal events of his life.

An even more intoxicating passion was, however, soon to engulf him, as he fell in love with his master's wife. Mme Parangon, the name he gives her in his autobiography and which means 'paragon' as well as being a size of type, was in part the reincarnation of Jeannette Rousseau. This time, though, his idolizing love was accompanied by strong physical desires for her. It is interesting to note that, when he recounts the episode in *Monsieur Nicolas*, he makes Colette several years younger than she actually was and also conceals the fact that she had a number of children. In Rétif's eyes she was too good for her somewhat brutal and womanizing husband and had also managed to preserve her 'virginal purity'. He depicts her as a friendly, kindred spirit, who shared his love of literature and particularly warmed to his expressive reading of such things as Corneille's heroic drama *Le Cid*. He would appear to have spent a lot of time in her company, and she is shown to be actively concerned for his welfare, to the extent of wanting to arrange a marriage with her younger sister Fanchette. Again, if we are to believe Rétif, he destroyed this singular chance of happiness when he gave way to the destructive force of passion in a frenzied and brutal attack upon her. It is hard to accept, as some biographers and critics have done, that the attack actually took place, as the scene is full of Racinian overtones and couched in the colourful language of fantasy. What is not in doubt is Rétif's awareness of his sensuality and the strong feelings of guilt which it aroused. 'As a child of Nature and of my father I was good. I was good as I grew within my worthy mother's womb. I left my birthplace and I became corrupt, like the once pure stream that flows through the streets gathering muck and filth as it goes.' At the time of the Jeannette Rousseau episode Rétif was between childhood and adolescence. This time he is between adolescence and adulthood. The former shepherd-boy now frequents the dance-halls of Auxerre, mixing with the lower orders and becoming, in his own eyes, ever more corrupted. In May 1753 he did, however, celebrate with his parents the successful completion of his apprenticeship. Soon, he was preparing himself for the altogether more tempting and dangerous world of Paris.

Rétif was neither eager nor confident when he set out to find work in Paris on 1st September, 1755, just two months before his twenty-first birthday. Indeed, he was to refer to the next ten years or so as his 'dead years', his 'years of nullity'. They were broken by the writing and subsequent publication of his first novel in 1767. His early impressions of Paris are most poignantly expressed in his semi-autobiographical novel *The Perverted Peasant*, published twenty years later. He comments on the filthy streets alongside more prosperous ones, on the enormous gulf between the rich and the poor, and on the general indifference of people towards each other which contributed to moral laxity. This is how he describes the lot of ordinary working people: 'The worker puts up day and night with the hardest labour, from which he knows only death will free him, in anticipation of spending Sunday at a pleasure-garden drinking revolting wine with the coarse and unappetising object of his affections.'

Rétif's first job was at the royal printing works in the galleries of the Louvre, where he earned about ninepence a day. The next year he doubled his wages by moving to another printer, but then quickly moved on again. He was working very long hours usually six days a week and felt he was becoming an automaton who might simply wear himself out and waste his life as a journeyman printer. Though he had a number of friends, several from his Auxerre days, he was leading a restless and rootless existence. Furthermore, his increasingly frequent contacts with an assortment of women, including prostitutes, made his sense of degeneration and worthlessness more acute. Rétif's boasts about his sexual prowess and even more exaggerated paternity are both comic and pathetic, revealing as they do an extraordinary capacity and need to indulge in fantasy. In 1768, for example, he claims to have had a relationship with a virtuous prostitute, Zéphire, whom he rescued and was about to marry when she died. For him she was the second incarnation of Jeannette Rousseau. Thus, the three most important figures in his 'unique passion', as he calls it, are the virgin, the married woman and the fallen woman. They are the embodiment of a love which purports to be timeless because unique, and they also mark the stages of his own progressive decline. Rétif was, in fact, fundamentally uncertain as to the nature of love; unable to reconcile his belief in the ideal with his notion of passion as a fatal force and at the same time as a vital affirmation of natural energy. His uncertainty in this matter was shared by a number of the major writers of the century.

In November 1759, after a short spell at a printing works in Dijon and three months unemployed in Paris, he returned to work as M. Parangon's foreman, Mme Parangon having died two years earlier. It was in Auxerre that he met Agnès Lebègue, the daughter of a bankrupt apothecary who had joined the army to escape his debts. They were married on 22nd April, 1760, and after a row with Parangon they moved to Paris a year later, their first daughter, Agnès, having been born in March of the same year. Their poverty, which was to prevent Rétif from attending his father's funeral in 1763, and the endlessly wretched accommodation which they were forced to take soured them both. According to Rétif, his marriage was an unhappy failure from the outset, partly as a result of infidelity on both sides, partly due to their fundamental incompatibility. Their frequent quarrels soon led to them living apart for considerable periods, with each more or less going his or her own way. His luck changed in July 1764 when he obtained the job as foreman of Quillau's printing-works where he supervised seventy compositors and helped build up the business from four to twelve presses. He was now earning nearly a pound a week and received a copy of each book they printed as well. It was in the November of that same year that his second daughter, Marion, was born. When, however, he sold his first novel to the bookseller, widow Duchesne, for £33 in 1767, he gave up his job believing that he would now earn his living as a writer.

It was whilst reading a novel by Mme Benoist, having

earlier read the proofs of several of Mme Riccoboni's sentimental novels, that Rétif felt that he could emulate these two ladies of letters. But when he started to write, he quickly discovered that he was able to produce almost nothing out of his own imagination, needing a 'muse' to stimulate him. In his case, this meant being aroused at the sight of a pretty woman to the point where desire precipitated intense creative activity. When he was writing *The New Abeilard*, for example, Mlle Londeau was his muse: 'Every evening I became intoxicated with the pleasure of seeing her, and the sight of her animated me. I wrote at night and the following morning with unbelievable ardour.' He also needed an incident, an event, something he had witnessed or been told to provide him with the basis for a story. Having gone home to Sacy in the summer of 1767 hoping to write another book, he produced nothing. Nature proved a distraction not a stimulus, so he quickly returned to the electrifying atmosphere of Paris. Yet, whatever difficulty he may have experienced in finding the appropriate inspiration and conditions for work, once he got going, there was no stopping him. In the course of the next seven years he published twelve works, writing some at incredible speed – *Lucile* in five days, *Fanchette's Foot* in twelve, *The Illegitimate Girl* in six. Indeed, he was to keep up and even increase that momentum almost until the end of his life, publishing in all over two hundred volumes before his death in 1806. They included many novels, essays proposing the reform of prostitution, the theatre, language etc., a number of plays, a huge collection of stories, anecdotes and incidents in the sixty-five volumes devoted to 'contemporary women', and last but not least, a significant number of autobiographical and semi-autobiographical works. Given that so many were written very fast and without much reflection, some even being composed straight onto the press, it is hardly surprising that their quality is extremely uneven. The worst are trite, sentimental and boring; the best are vivid, striking in their detailed observation, and full of remarkable insights into moral and psychological problems which preoccupied eighteenth-century writers in general. A number also contain engravings specially commissioned and supervised by Rétif which add greatly to their interest.

Rétif never became rich from writing. Too often he was at the mercy of printers, booksellers, engravers and, like many other writers of the period, the victim of pirate editions. Yet his energy never flagged, and, as a result, the extraordinary labour that his enormous output involved inevitably took its toll of his health. Furthermore, the effects of recurrent venereal disease and other major physical ailments, the steadily worsening relationship with his wife, and his involvement in his daughter, Agnès's, marital strife added to his suffering and increased his feelings of bitterness. He thought that his wife had turned both his daughters against him, and this merely strengthened his commitment to his work as a way of trying to forget his sorrows. Writing of his misery in 1782 he comments: 'I was killing myself with work, to distract myself, having no other pleasure, no other relaxation than a short daily walk on the Ile St Louis, during which I engraved on the stones my suffering and the fears caused by parts of my work.' Rétif here refers to complaints he received from readers who thought they could identify themselves in his anecdotes of contemporary life. In November 1785 Agnès left him for good, and they were divorced eight years later. From then on he lived with or near his daughter Marion. What money he had earned from writing he later placed in promissory notes issued by the Revolutionary government; when they became worthless in 1796 he was ruined. In 1798 he obtained a job in the police department responsible for the interception of letters, which lasted for a little over two years. Thereafter, his health steadily declined, and he died on 6th February, 1806 at the age of seventy-one. In the last twenty-five years or so of this life he had become the friend of several writers and prominent figures, including Beaumarchais, Grimod de la Reynière, Mercier and Fanny de Beauharnais. The peasant's son from Burgundy had made his mark, but perhaps at some considerable cost to himself as the obituary in the *Journal de Paris* of 9th February, 1806 intimated: 'M. Rétif, it is said, depicted himself in several of his works; of that we know nothing. What we can say of him is what he said of one of his heroes: had he remained in his village, he would have been less famous but happier.'

Rétif's impulse to write was complex in its origins. The desire to emulate the achievement of authors he read was present from an early age, as was the tendency to fantasize as a way of giving vent to strong emotions. From the age of eighteen he also began to record in notebooks the most important events of his life; an activity which was subsequently to be developed into a major autobiographical undertaking, the equal in scope and perhaps in importance of that of Jean-Jacques Rousseau. Finally, one must not forget that Rétif increasingly wrote with a strong sense of guilt. He had acquired in childhood, both from his father and elder brothers, clear and austere moral precepts. As he grew up, his intellectual curiosity was awakened and developed by his reading and by those he met; and his life-style, expectations and attitudes were transformed in the context of urban life. Gradually he worked out, or rather cobbled together, a new morality based on enlightenment principles; but in the recesses of his mind there remained powerful images associated with sin, punishment and damnation. That is why so much of his autobiographical writing is dominated by a mood of fatalism, the result of a sense of degeneration and worthlessness. For Rétif, writing was a fundamentally obsessive and compulsive activity, which in many respects may have had a therapeutic effect. However fatalistic he was about his own destiny, he seemed to retain a belief in writing as a purposeful and redemptive activity. Not only did literature serve as a means of exposing through confession his degradation and of converting it, as he hoped, into moral example; it also became a life-raft in the face of mounting difficulties and worries and a means of preserving his identity.

His reputation as a writer rests essentially on a relatively limited number of books. As an observer of Parisian life in the second half of the eighteenth century, he is almost without equal. *Les Nuits de Paris, or the Nocturnal Spectator* (1788–94), for example, stand alongside the enormous collection of stories devoted to contemporary women, from which *The Ploughman's Wife* is taken, as Rétif's attempt to record the manners and morals of the period. *The Nocturnal Spectator* also contains his personal account of what he witnessed in the streets and his reactions to key events during the Revolution.

He is fearful of mob violence and often confused and inconsistent in his reactions, but this seems to make his testimony all the more personal and authentic. *The Perverted Peasant, or the Dangers of the Town* (1775) established him as a novelist of some importance. Inspired by his reading of Richardson's *Pamela* and seeking deliberately to counter the confident, optimistic tone of Marivaux's *The Parvenu Peasant* (1735–36), Rétif drew heavily on his own experience in this moralizing and somewhat melodramatic novel. He was to work on it over twenty years, fusing it ultimately with *The Perverted Peasant Girl*. In it, town and country life and the forces of good and evil are starkly contrasted, yet the novel is full of moral ambiguity. On the one hand, it is a defence of country life, on the other, it represents Paris as a place where the individual enjoys freedom; and it is in part based on the premise of upward social mobility. The overt social message is couched in the language of Christian orthodoxy, but it is everywhere permeated with enlightenment relativism. *Monsieur Nicolas, or the Human Heart Laid Bare* (1794–97) is the culmination of ever-deepening commitment to autobiography. He was not, he claims, inspired by Rousseau; adding that his is the truthful account of the life of an ordinary man, whereas Rousseau's *Confessions* were the fictionalised story of a great man. Again, there is an insistence upon the moral value of the work, as the sub-title perhaps implies. And in his introduction Rétif argues that he is writing a work of philosophy and of natural history with which he will rival Buffon, Montesquieu and Voltaire. 'These are not my *Confessions* I am making, they are the workings of the human heart which I lay bare.' Despite these assertions and his reference to the sacrifice of himself that the work involves, the book is nonetheless a profoundly egocentric one. Already in his notebooks and in his 'Inscriptions' on the walls of the Ile St Louis, subsequently recorded and published as a diary, Rétif revealed a desperate need to preserve his memories. In *Monsieur Nicolas* that need is movingly expressed: 'The future is for me a terrifying and bottomless pit which I dare not sound. But I do as those who fear water, I throw in a stone: an event which actually happened to me. I write it down, then add: 'What shall I be thinking at the same hour, on the same day in a year's time?' This idea excites me. I follow its development throughout the year, and every day is the anniversary of some event, each day brings a new pleasure.' Rétif's pleasure at recapturing lost time and at the fusion of past and present emotion offers a striking prefiguration of what Proust was to explore in his masterpiece a little over a century later. And though his fatalistic outlook and despair at his decline are pronounced, his intense and sustained literary activity is affirmatory and optimistic. Moreover, fatalism and despair about the self as a moral entity are matched by an equally persistent concern with the continuity of the self and by a strong desire to achieve some sense of identity and coherence. Removed from the natural world of his childhood, and from the relative security and stability of family and community life, Rétif discovered that he needed to write in order to survive as a personality.

In the light of these remarks, *My Father's Life* will, one hopes, be more easily understood and appreciated. *The Ploughman's Wife* has been included as an interesting companion piece, devoted as it is to his mother. *My Father's Life* is a work of both celebration and atonement; yet it gives us at the same time a fuller picture of rural life in eighteenth-century France than any other published work. Flawed though it is in part by sentimentality and the urge to moralize, it illuminates the peasant world from within and allows us to experience it at first hand.

RICHARD VEASEY
School of European Studies
University of Sussex

MY FATHER'S LIFE

Some celebrate warriors who have triumphed in armed combat; academies bestow prizes on writers who have enhanced the reputation of former ministers and of distinguished men of letters. I, on the other hand, shall pay tribute to the memory of an honourable man whose virtue was of the ordinary, 'everyday' kind, one might say. He was simply upright and hardworking, and it is qualities such as these that are the bedrock of every society and without which heroes would die of hunger.

I also give a new impulse to filial piety, for if the son of every man of a certain standing felt obliged to write the story of his father's life, it would have a most beneficial effect. Is there a father, knowing that his son was to be the truthful historian of his own life, who would not achieve some virtue, would not perform some good deeds? Would he not do this in the hope at least of preventing his name from being tarnished by the very person who was to perpetuate it? It would doubtless be a most powerful means of curbing the rapid corruption of our morals.

Humble mortal who was virtuous without show, did good by inclination and lived frugally by choice, my father! Receive the homage that the least worthy of your sons dares to offer in your memory.

BOOK 1

Edme Rétif, son of Pierre and of Anne Simon, was born on November 16th, 1692 at Nitri which formed part of the estate of the Abbey of Molême in Tonnerois. His father, a man of moderate means, was of pleasant appearance and an entertaining conversationalist. Everyone sought his company and when they could not persuade him to visit them, *they* came to him. But because he enjoyed such popularity, he quickly developed a taste for easy living and as a result his affairs suffered.

Edme was not clever. His father thought him stupid and neglected him, but the young man's character was sound. He had such good sense and judgement that at the age of twelve, worried by the deterioration in the affairs of the household and moved by the tears of the most affectionate of mothers, he took things in hand in order to prevent total ruin. His father's conduct, though acceptable in the eyes of the world at large, provided him with a salutary lesson. Yet it did not diminish his respect for him, and indeed he carried that virtue to such limits that the following proverb is still remembered in Nitri: 'He fears his parents as Edmond feared his father.'

But this father, who was so well-disposed to strangers, was an awesome figure in his own home. He would command with a single look which one had to learn to interpret, and his daughters, of whom there were three, were scarcely ever treated indulgently. His wife, on the other hand, was so deeply imbued with respect for her husband that she looked upon him simply as her beloved master. Although she was from a superior family, related to the Coeurderoi, several of whom are still presidents in the law courts of Burgundy, she would rush to satisfy his every whim, And when her work was done the reward she received from her imperious husband was the simple command 'Go and rest yourself'. Yet a sovereign's accolade to a courtier could not have been more gratifying.

3

But if Anne Simon respected her husband as her master, she
was more than rewarded by the tenderness shown her by her
children. All of them supported her and at the slightest upset
her daughters would gather round and wipe away her tears.
Yet when, from time to time, a less than respectful remark
about their father escaped their lips, Anne immediately adopted a severe tone and admonished them sternly.

As for her son, he was her true consolation. What love he
showed in obeying her exactly as she obeyed her husband.
Indeed, she would sometimes say to her daughters 'Why do
you consider me worthy of praise since I do no more for my
husband than my son does for me? Dear children, if ever I
were unfortunate enough to think of rebelling against my
husband, I would only have to say to myself – 'He is
Edmond's father' – to dispel such thoughts altogether.'

Edmond's way of showing his love for his mother was
always effective. If he was present when her husband was
grumbling at her, he did not attempt to win his father round
with a show of affection that would have been rebuffed.
Instead, he embraced his mother and chose that moment to
tell her that he had successfully completed some task or other
which she had asked him to perform. The proud master of the
house was then more willing to speak to his wife in a gentler
tone and withdraw quietly.

Edmond's first education outside the home was given him
by two equally respectable figures, the priest of Nitri and his
schoolmaster, the worthy Berthier, whose name after eighty
years is still remembered with gratitude in the neighbourhood. Any parish which has servants such as these is fortunate
indeed. What a splendid race they are! The schoolmaster was
married and had numerous children of his own, yet he
performed his duties to the letter in a generous and friendly
manner. His standing as a family man won him respect, and
his conduct afforded the best proof that celibacy is not a
desirable state for those whose job it is to teach the young
or even for those who are ministers of God. Far from it, since
every bachelor is an egotist and cannot avoid being one. Yet
the virtue shown by some priests in their celibacy is truly
superhuman. They are doubtless worthy of the highest
respect, but should one make virtue so demanding? Will the

day ever dawn . . .? Alas! some may even consider me a criminal for expressing such a patriotic desire.

I wish to portray the venerable Berthier solely through his actions. I have already described them in *L'Ecole des Pères* which D.L.H., les S—— and les Ling—— thought a bad novel, but which is in reality a repository of the most heroic virtues. It would indeed be a bad novel, but let those who find it difficult to accept the truthfulness of others take heed and accept that it is not a novel. It was written from the heart and records what I have heard. If it is a bad book, virtue has made it so and you must count yourself above her. Here now is the passage in which the worthy Berthier is depicted. It follows on from one which I will introduce at the end of the present work and which offers a similar portrait of the venerable parish priest.

'Our schoolmaster prepared the ground for the priest and completed his work. Let me explain myself. First of all he taught the children the most elementary things and gave the older boys and girls simple lessons about everyday life and behaviour between husband and wife, brothers and sisters etc. As he was married and the father of a large family, his advice bore the stamp of his own experience. It became known subsequently, however, that everything was worked out in advance with the priest. Twice a year there were holidays for harvest and for grape picking. Only a few pupils returned to school after the two harvests and most waited until all the main jobs had been completed. The two fixed dates for the closure and reopening of the school were June 1st and October 20th. There were no lessons on those two days as the worthy old man spent the time talking to us. And whenever I recall what he said I am still moved.

His talk in June revolved around the wrongs one might do one's neighbour during harvest-time and the ways one might fill the hours which were not spent in work.

– Children, he would begin, we are about to separate for more than four months. Work in the fields awaits you and you must help your fathers and mothers who have brought you into the world, who feed you and who endure cold and heat, hunger and thirst on your behalf. As good parents they will leave only

the easiest jobs to you during the pleasantest season of the
year, keeping the hardest work for themselves. How different
they are from tradesmen in towns who burden their appren-
tices with the harshest and most wearisome tasks and who, as
a result, exhaust and even damage young bodies which are not
yet fully developed. And so, dear children, some of you are
about to begin, others to continue a gentle apprenticeship in
the noblest and most useful of arts which God instituted and
which he watches over. May you feel in your hearts, dearest
children, its true worth and never dishonour it. Never degrade
it through bad behaviour, by being dishonest, nasty, wicked,
or by damaging other men's property, either yourselves or
with your animals. That is the most important thing, my dear
young friends. You are about to spend whole days in the
woods and fields with scatter-brains of your own age, far out
of sight of your mothers and fathers who would keep you
fearful of God and men. One ne'er-do-well can, by his
influence and example, corrupt half the children in the parish.
Pupils, I beg you in God's name, for your own and for my
sake, I who love you all, remember sometimes on these
occasions the lessons you received here. Try to remember
how our good priest taught you what is right and how poor
old Berthier did everything in his power to support him.
Listen, my friends. When people give you bad advice or when
some wicked thought comes into your head, stop a moment
and say to yourself: What am I about to do? Suppose I saw
someone about to do the same thing on our land, would I be
happy about it? What would I do to him? What would I say?
Perhaps at this very moment, as a punishment for what I am
tempted to do, God allows someone else to do the same or
worse to us. How can I complain about a rogue if I am one
myself? If someone saw me, what would they think? But
suppose no one can see me. God sees you, you wretch. God
sees you and yet you are not afraid. My dear children, no
young boy or girl who tries to remember what I told them
will ever go astray. We are all brothers in this parish. We must
all watch over what belongs to others. What a lovely community ours would be if it were like that. Well then, dear
pupils, let each of you vie with the others for the honour of
setting out along that road. Let Nitri be an example to the

surrounding villages and may others only ever mention our name in praise. Each of you will benefit at the expense of the wicked and will gain what they lose as a punishment for their wickedness. That is how, even in this life, good conduct earns its reward. I beg you children, spare me the sorrow of learning that one of you paid no attention to what I said. And again, I beg you, with tears in my eyes, to feel for an old man who must answer before God for all the sins that you commit and which he might have prevented, but from which he cannot discharge you.

Let me remind you that you have just completed seven or eight months in school. Try not to forget them, children. When you lead your animals to the fields, take with you your shortened Bibles and if you meet, read several chapters together. On Sundays, do a few pages of writing. It is to your own advantage that you work, preparing for the day when you will have affairs of your own to look after. Farewell, dear pupils, and as I give you my own feeble blessing, may God grant you his blessing. Let us pray together before we part that his power may be confirmed in us. After the prayer, he kissed each one of us and sent us home.

His talk, when school reopened, was in two parts. In the first, this honest master recounted all the misdeeds which his pupils had committed during the summer. He reproached each one of them by name, or rather mildly rebuked him and urged him to make amends for his misdemeanours. I should tell you that during the holidays the worthy old man constantly kept his eye on all of us and knew exactly what we had done. The trouble he went to in order to find out was astonishing, but he was careful and we were never aware of him. He would never admonish anyone during the period of his 'suspended authority', as he called it. He gave a full account of his findings to the good priest and together they worked out the atonement for the sin and the improvement of the sinner. But it was all done as secretly as if they were dealing with affairs of state. The second part of his talk was given up to exhortations about the best use of our time. Then he allotted pupils their places, putting the most ignorant on the bench nearest to him and the cleverest on the one which

was furthest away. He did this, he said, because he felt that the
ignorant should be able to listen to what he taught the others.
It was also the front row which recited last. Here then are the
most important parts of the last talk he gave just three months
before he died.

– Here we are reunited once again children. How agreeable
for me this day would be, on which my pleasures and my
labours rebegin, were you all worthy of praise; if I could
congratulate myself that not one of you had disregarded the
words of a poor old man who begged you, hands clasped in
prayer, not to burden him in the eyes of the great Judge with
sins that he should have prevented you from committing. Oh
children! you stand less in awe of God than of men, yet men
are nothing. For the most part they are ignorant of the
blackness of a deed, yet God sees into the innermost recesses
of our hearts. You have offended against our loving father,
who has given us the harvest for our nourishment and
without whose providence nothing would have prospered, at
the very moment at which you received bread from his hands.
You have offended him in your brothers, your friends and
your fellow villagers; in those with whom you are united as in
one family every Sunday as you take bread, which the
minister of God has blessed, and which is distributed as a
symbol of communion and fraternity. Oh children! have
some of you thus become traitors in the house of God? You
should have refused the bread the moment you wished harm
upon any of those to whom he swore love in your name. You
should not have come near him in church, nor have remained
in his presence, for in this way you would at least have
avoided the crime of the damned apostle; you would not have
defiled the temple and the sacrament. I am unable to continue
and my tears will express what I cannot say, children.

Then he named each of those who had done wrong to his
neighbour. One he rebuked for having given his oxen sheaves
of oats which did not belong to him, another for having
allowed his to graze in someone else's lucerne and sainfoin,
the next for having quarrelled, and yet another for fighting
and for having maltreated and injured his friend's oxen. He

had driven them hard, yoked to the plough, in order to spare
his own, and had worked long hours the days he was
ploughing his own land. He also shortened the working day
when those with whom he shared the implements were
ploughing their land. Someone else had encroached on his
neighbour's land by one or two furrows or had taken a few
bundles or a few sheaves from the edge of a field. Another had
eaten grapes or fruit growing next to his. Several were
rebuked for improper remarks and swearing, as well as for
liberties they had taken with the girls, and for the vulgar
language they had used when talking to them. Others were
chided for their scandal-mongering and their lies. Finally, he
reprimanded those who had been absent from services and, as
he made each one show him their books and papers, he
admonished those who had neglected their reading and writing. He turned his attention to the girls after the boys. The
behaviour of our young village girls was quite innocent and
they scarcely ever had any of the faults of the young men.
Almost the only thing for which they could be reproached
was the use of their tongue, and it is for this that the
schoolmaster reprimanded them, as well, on occasions, as for
their laziness and half-heartedness. If one of them had done
something worse, he would single her out for admonition.
Would that they remained the same in womanhood as they
were as girls, he would sometimes say. It is the men,
however, who spoil them with their bad example, who
dominate them and make them bitter. When he had told each
person how to make amends for the wrong he or she had
done, he went on to the second part of his talk.

– Well children, let us not be discouraged. The right way of
atoning for one's sins is by doing good. Let us renew
ourselves, acquire fresh habits, forget the year that has passed
in the one to come, during which we will improve ourselves.
This is the fiftieth year I have been in this school where I knew
your fathers and even some of your grandfathers. I have seen
nothing but improvement from year to year except for these
last few years, which may perhaps be attributed to the fact that
I have reached seventy-five years of age and cannot do my
duty by you as well as I did by your predecessors. One might in

fact say that my work is completed and that my end is in sight.
May God grant each of you an old age like mine, with no
other infirmities than the gradual dimming of the fire of life
within. How long, children, do you imagine my seventy-five
years have seemed? You who are young imagine that it has
been a long time. In my eyes at this moment, it seems only
to have been a day. It feels as if it were only yesterday that I
was your age, still a child. At thirty my youth seemed
further away than it does today. My friends, without the
consolation of knowing that I have lived a good life, I should
be sad at this moment. But I am like the vine-grower who
has endured heat and thirst, bathed in sweat, and who only
experiences joy at the ending of the day and the approach of
night. Reflect on it, children. Life is only a day. You are in
the morning of your lives and I am in the evening of mine.
Others are at midday, aware of neither morning or evening
and experiencing only the heat of midday which invigorates
and intoxicates them. Be good, children, so that evening and
the coming of night do not make you fearful. My friends,
how dreadful the approach of death is for the wicked man,
but what a comfort it brings to whoever has done good,
served God, and helped his neighbour. He is like the honest
labourer who receives his day's wages, certain of being
praised by the head of the household and of receiving a
greater reward than his pay.

Each age has its corresponding duties. The old man
prepares for death by crowning his life with acts of devotion;
the father supports his family, raises his children and gives
them a good education. But the only duty of the child is to
work for himself and further the efforts that are made on his
behalf. That is your situation, children. Let us consider what
we can do this year to achieve our objective. So that each of
you may continue to make progress, what each one does will
be looked at, and you will go up a row as soon as you have
understood the lessons you are doing.

Such were the talks given by this honest teacher who, with
the wise priest who chose him, is now in God's care. You
should have seen what the men of Nitri were like in those
days. One can still see the last survivors amongst us but they

are becoming rarer. The purity of the language which disting-
uishes this community from its neighbours and which has
only altered slightly since that time is due to their instruction
which spread throughout the community. It is the very image
of that purity of morals which they strove to foster.

What do you think that honest fellow received from us as
his monthly salary (for we never had free schools in this area
as they have elsewhere)? Three sous a month if the child
hadn't yet learnt to write and five sous for those who had.
That was his reward for his fatherly concern. He never asked
for payment and some parents were uncharitable enough not
to give him anything for their children. The community
added fifty bushels of wheat and fifteen of barley to his
income each year, which might have been worth seventy to
seventy-five livres at that time. As a result, the honest fellow
had scarcely enough to live on, but he never complained.'

This is the story my worthy father would tell us over and
over again in our childhood, with tears in his eyes as he paid
tribute to that virtuous schoolmaster of his. All these things
are so deeply imprinted upon my memory; and whatever I
may have written that is good comes not from me but from
my father, my grandfather, lawyer Rétif; from upright
teachers such as these whose wisdom in its essence was the
purest moral law. You will discover, if you turn to L'Ecole des
Pères the importance that these worthy citizens attached to
having a good priest and a good schoolmaster, and you will
also come to realise that the well-being of a rural community,
high moral standards and, as a result, the prosperity of the
State are dependent upon the example of these two men. They
are the ones who create good fathers and especially the
schoolmaster, if he is like Berthier.

Pierre Rétif was too intelligent not to notice his son's true
worth and the goodness of his heart. He admired him
therefore, yet at the same time preserved his own dignity, and
this was perhaps beneficial if one is to judge by the results.
When they went on a short journey together Pierre would
walk ahead alone and only utter the occasional remark about
things they saw. His son followed respectfully behind, not
daring to ask him any questions.

The terrible winter of 1709 finally brought home to Pierre

his son's real value. Since he was a pleasure-seeking man who was always a little short of money, he had sold his wheat early, and consequently gained nothing from the exhorbitant rise in the price which occurred six months later. On the contrary, he was obliged to buy some in for his own needs during a period of two months, having kept only just enough to see him through until the early crop was ready. He had done just the same with the finer grains. Edmond was passionately fond of horses. Indeed, he was so fond of that noble animal, the companion of his labours, that he could not bear to see it deprived of its barley and oats, as his father had decided it should be. He therefore hid a considerable amount in old barrels and urged his friends, whose fathers resembled his own, to do the same. One should not look upon this as an act of childishness; it was a precautionary measure of the utmost importance in a country in which, even today, domestic animals are so neglected that they are incapable of cultivating the land properly. I will explain what I mean later. Pierre Rétif was too negligent of his affairs to notice the considerable quantity of finer grains his son was putting aside. The latter learned yet another lesson from this, namely that someone could steal from his father without him realising it.

When everything was killed by frost, Edmond, sick at heart, went to look at the corn that had cost him so much effort (he was then sixteen and half). Not a single shoot remained, but the soil had been so broken down by the frost that it seemed ready for sowing again. Edmond suddenly had an idea. On his own initiative, saying nothing about it to anyone in the household, he took the plough out onto the land. He let the shares pass lightly through the soil and sowed a mixture of barley and oats, as thinly as he could. He was laughed at and his father grumbled and forbad him to continue. Edmond obeyed, but urged his friends to carry out what he no longer dared do. The results exceeded all their hopes and saved the village. The thinly sown seeds produced enormous tufts and the barley was of a size that had not been seen before. The few acres that Edmond had sown before his father stopped him produced sufficient good grain, once the barley had been sifted from the oats, to feed the family. Thus the young man forestalled the total ruin of the household and at the same time saved the community. If Pierre Rétif had given him his head, he would have made him rich, as several individuals had offered to give up fields to those who were willing to sow them for the usual return, which at that time was a quarter of the yield.

Pierre, more convinced than ever of his son's great good sense, finally admitted that this precious attribute was worth more than intelligence. He was the local magistrate of Nitri, a position which cost him a lot, since the sitting always took place in his house and at his expense. There was no other tavern-keeper than the judge. And so he decided to pay more attention to Edmond's education.

He had a relation whose family name was the same as ours and who was a lawyer in Noyers. He was a clever man, well-known for his probity and firmness. He was extremely rich, and his grandsons today hold important positions in Dauphiné. It was to this man that Pierre entrusted a son, whom he might well have educated himself had he liked his pleasures less. He did so on one condition; that, having spent the winter studying, his son was to return home in the spring to do the ploughing and to supervise all the other work.

For my part, I would not have the temerity to criticise my ancestor's behaviour in this instance. Although Edmond Rétif did not follow this example himself with his children, he only ever referred to it with respectful admiration and admitted that it was as a result of his father's behaviour that he had preserved his own innocence during his six months stay in the town.

At the end of the first six months, Pierre did not fail to ask the lawyer to send his son home, and he returned with the following letter, of which we still have the original safely preserved:

My dear cousin,

I am sending home a good lad. He will never be an intellectual prodigy, but I guarantee that he will be a good judge and a good husband and father in due course, better indeed than you, and that he will be thoroughly honest in every respect. As for his progress, he is capable of taking in anything to do with business and practical matters. But as far

as the things which you enjoy so much are concerned, he is an
absolute fool.

I congratulate you on his qualities and on his faults, his
faults, do you understand? Those faults will restore to the
family what others have lost, and I say this without reproach,
my dear Pierre. You know I am fond of you, even though I
have sometimes been critical. We have generous hearts in our
family and we forgive everything except dishonour; but by
God's grace, we have suffered none.

Your son has our heart and that of the Coeur-de-Roy, and
you yourself know well what that is worth. I send my
greetings to Anne and congratulate her a hundred times more
than you for having such a son. You tell her that! And by jove
make sure you do! I insist, and just remember, I can be a real
Rétif when I want to be. Make sure you tell her then, as I shall
check up on you. Climb down off that high horse of yours, or
I shall knock you off when I next visit you. I almost forgot to
mention what I think is your son's real virtue. It is that he
respects and honours you as the image of God and loves you
beyond all compare. In closing, I thank you for having given
me the opportunity of offering such an example to my two
lads.

Farewell Pierrot. I am truly yours, and send my best wishes
to my cousin Anne Simon and my love to the little *Rétives*.
We must remain true to the family name for honour's sake.

Rétif, lawyer,
Noyers, March 10th, 1710.

Once he was back in his father's house, Edmond was as
eager as ever to rebegin work in the fields after his easy and
quiet life in town. Everything had deteriorated during his six
months absence; the plough horses were in a bad state, the
granaries and stables in disorder. And so this young man, who
had just left an opulent household where he had been treated
as a son, found himself working harder than ever. But a love
of work, which he retained until the end of his life, his tender
feelings for his mother and the great respect which he had for
his father raised his courage to such a level that he set
everything to rights within eighty days. He spent fifteen days

caring for the horses before he could use them again, but, due
to his tireless efforts, all was well in the end.

Shall I tell of the tears he shed when he saw how a splendid
horse had become a bag of bones in his absence? Why should
such a display of emotion towards a useful animal, which
repays friendship with friendship as well as with its labour, be
considered ridiculous? Bressan, a large and beautiful horse,
had almost human intelligence and an attachment to his young
master which was stronger than many human friendships.
Edmond had only to give a simple command to be obeyed,
and one could see that there was a bond between them. One
day, a cart loaded with manure got stuck near the dung-heap.
Two ploughboys had tried all the coaxing and all the curses
they knew and had broken their whip without being able to
get the four horses out. Then Edmond appeared. 'Get out of
the way, you brutes', he shouted. He kissed the horse, stroked
it and let it get its wind. When it had recovered, he put his
hand on the shaft, pretended to heave and said 'Come on
Bressan, come on old friend'. Hearing a voice he knew so
well, the noble animal made a sudden effort and pulled the cart
some twenty yards on his own, believing he was being
helped. He had to be restrained, otherwise he would have
exhausted himself. You can well imagine how Edmond
grieved when he returned home and discovered this faithful
animal in such a wretched condition.

Busy with his jobs on the land, Edmond did not share the
pleasures of his contemporaries. But there is one agreeable
emotion that even the hardest toil cannot dispel, for love is the
very life-blood of honest souls, is coloured by their own
temperament, and becomes the most attractive of their virtues.

There lived in Nitri a young girl called Catherine
Gautherin, who was virtuous, hard-working and whose face
seemed full of laughter. She was more radiant than a freshly
opened rose and had an attractive figure, although she was a
little on the plump side. In a word, she was a most attractive
girl. Edmond noticed her and was struck as much by her
qualities as by her charms. In the village where they lived, it
was the custom (and still is) to pester the pretty girls. The
boys would take everything they could from them, their

posies, their rings, their bags etc. Coming out of mass one Sunday morning, Edmond noticed a rival snatching Catherine's posy, and he was jealous. He went up to her and, taking out his button-hole, offered it to her saying, 'Here are some rose buds that will look better on you than on me'. The young girl blushed. 'At least let us share them', she replied. The button-hole was made up of red and white roses and she kept the white ones. Scarcely had Edmond left her out of modesty, when a bold young man tried to snatch her new posy from her. Catherine, who had relinquished the first one almost without resistance, now tried her hardest to keep this one. 'Just because it was Edmond's', the young man said bitterly.

All this got to the ears of Edmond's stern father, who was suprised that his son should have dared, at his age, to look at a girl without first asking his permission. He said nothing at lunch, but made discreet enquiries that day and learned from a busybody that Edmond had spoken three times to Catherine Gautherin since his return from Noyers. The next day, as Edmond, in shirtsleeves and already mounted on Bressan, was about to set off with the plough, his father came up to him. 'Give me your whip', he said. 'Here it is, father', Edmond replied. The three savage strokes he then received from someone as strong as his father cut his shirt in three places, staining it with blood. Edmond just heaved a sigh, and Pierre, calmly handing back the whip, simply said, 'Just remember that', and went in again without adding another word.

Edmond did not know at all what he had done to deserve such a harsh punishment. But paying no attention to his wounds, he went on his way and worked all day long as usual. On his return, Anne Simon noticed his shirt and imagined he must have had an accident. She let out a cry, but Edmond reassured her saying, 'It's nothing, mother'. She questioned the ploughboys and discovered what had happened, but not the reason for it. She then came back to her son and began to dress his wounds which needed attention as pieces of material had gone right into his skin. At that moment her husband appeared and with tears in her eyes she turned to him and said 'See what you have done'. Looking away, Pierre replied 'That's how I deal with young men who flirt'.

Edmond and his mother had to work out for themselves the full significance of that laconic remark.

Yet this man, who appeared so hard on the outside, was in fact tender-hearted. He came out of the house again and went into the garden. After his mother had dressed his wounds, Edmond, who neglected nothing, went to see if any plants needed watering or if any beds needed hoeing. He went into the garden, but because it was so large and full of bushy shrubs, he neither saw his father nor was seen by him. But at last Edmond noticed him, leaning against a tree which he himself had planted, one hand on his brow, the other wiping away his tears. Never before had he seen his father crying, and he was so suprised at his father's tears that he felt that the whole world had turned upside down. 'I was much too hard on him', he heard his father say. Deeply moved by this, but afraid of showing himself, he fell to his knees and said inwardly to himself 'Dear father, I have cost you these tears, yet I am so happy because I know you love me'. He then stretched out his arms towards him, still hidden from view. As his father moved, he got up and went to the other end of the garden, where he found another piece of ground that needed digging, and set to work.

His father must have heard him because he walked over to him, took the spade from his hands and said 'You've done enough work for one day, my son. Go and rest now and let me finish it'.

Never before had Pierre uttered the words 'my son'. Never before had he done any digging or pulled a single weed in the garden, but on this occasion he finished the whole piece. Trembling with joy, Edmond went to tell his mother what had happened. And because he was such a favourite with his sisters, they all shared his happiness. From time to time Anne Simon would open the window and watch her husband digging. 'He's finishing it. He's finishing Edmond's piece. I told you he was a kind father at heart. It's because he didn't want his son to have to finish it. Oh what a good father he is!' 'Oh, what a good father he is', the children replied.

Whenever Edmond recalled this scene, tears filled his eyes and he would bless his father for being so strict. 'If he hadn't been', he often used to say to us, 'I might perhaps have become too independent, like so many others. He stopped my misbe-

haviour from the outset, and this firmness on his part was
necessary as my attachment was already quite strong.'

It is true that Catherine was a fine girl and she made Jacques
Berthier, one of the sons of the worthy schoolmaster, very
happy. But at the time, could one really have known her true
worth?

Considering that he was such an awesome figure, Pierre
could show great kindness, and he admired acts of generosity
above all else. As often happens with fathers who are particularly clever, his son was very quiet. A thoughtful child hardly
ever dares show any initiative in the presence of such a well-
informed father, who is only too ready to pick him up on his
slightest mistake. Edmond, who had the kindliest disposition,
was so compassionate towards those less fortunate than
himself that, at the age of ten, he gave his clothes to the son of
a poor beggar who was completely naked. My father's eldest
sister often used to talk to me about this characteristic of his.
Pierre also used to praise his son for it and would chuck him
under the chin as a sign of affection. But I would like to
mention another example of his tender compassion which was
almost inexhaustible, if I can put it that way.

An unfortunate fellow once committed an unpremeditated
murder, for which, as a result, he was pardonable. But an
ignorant peasant isn't capable of drawing such distinctions.
The man was put in a most unusual prison, which had never
before in living memory been needed in Nitry. It was in fact
used as a pigsty, though it had no roof. The murderer was put
inside this huge upturned cask and his feet were pushed
through a hole and fixed with iron bands, which the village
blacksmith made. Day and night, the poor fellow was left
there moaning. Young Edmond, moved by compassion,
comforted him and took him some fruit so that he might have
a little more to eat than his ordinary food. One day, when
everyone had gone into the fields, the child stayed behind near
the cask and said to the prisoner 'Can't you get out then,
mister?' 'Alas, no', he replied, 'My feet are fixed through this
hole and the nails had been driven in very firmly. If only I had
some pincers.' The child then went and fetched some, and the
man freed his legs. 'Can't you lift the cask up?' Edmond
asked. 'No my child, it's too heavy, but if only I had a pick.'

The child went and fetched a pick and handed it through the hole where the food was usually passed. The man then dug a hole, got out under the cask, and said to Edmond as he fled 'God bless you, my child'. He was never heard of again.

When the others returned, they noticed that he had escaped, but didn't know who had helped him. The child was frightened when he heard them talking about it and took care not to say anything. Thorough enquiries were made to find out who had freed the prisoner, but nothing was discovered. There was, however, in the village a most unpleasant man called D—— who had it in for a certain L——. Having involved one of his friends in the plot, both of them swore that it was L—— who had helped the prisoner to escape, and so L—— was placed in the cask.

As soon as the boy heard what had happened and why, he went to his mother in tears and confessed that he had given the prisoner the pincers and the pick, and that L—— had been nowhere near him. Anne Simon, fearing her husband's reaction, was rather troubled. But having gone out of her way to mollify Pierre, she told him about it, making the most of every detail which was in Edmond's favour. 'Where is he?' cried Pierre. The good-hearted woman believed that her son was doomed, but there was no point trying to delay things. He had to be sent for, and she went to meet him, and sheltered him with her own body.

'Edmond', his father said to him, 'your action in freeing the prisoner was unlawful, but for a lad of your age it was a good deed, and, if it was to be done, I am glad that my son should have done it rather than someone else. However, owning up in order to save an innocent person would be counted a good deed were it done by a man of forty, even though it is only right and proper. You can go now, I am very pleased with you.' And as his son turned away, he gave him his blessing. Whereupon, Anne Simon, beside herself with joy, fell to her knees before her husband and said 'You have given him your blessing. He will be happy all his life. And I am still more grateful to you, as my son's life is dearer to me than my own.'

A half year passed by almost without incident, except for a coversation which Edmond had one evening with old Brasdargent, who was one hundred and five and still active enough to take a cart out into the fields to gather up sheaves. Edmond, who was returning from another field further away with his own cart, came upon the old man loading up. Inspired by a feeling of respect for his venerable appearance, he stopped and went to help him.

'You've come at just the right moment', the centenarian said, 'the last few sheaves have to be loaded right on top and I know I can't reach up that far.'

Once the cart was loaded, they came back together. Edmond walked at a respectful distance behind this man, who had witnessed the birth of his grandfather and his father. This was indeed the first thought that came into his head and which inspired such deep respect. The old man broke the silence, as he pointed up to the sky and said, 'Have you read the Bible, my child?' 'Oh yes, father Brasdargent, I know it almost by heart.' 'Good, good, my child. You know, then, who made all that, the God of Abraham, of Isaac and of Jacob. He spake and it was made. I have to look up in wonder. Oh, how I love a clear night. It reveals to me the Lord of Creation. Daylight only shows me what he has made, but a beautiful night like this reveals God himself. Each one of those stars reveals him to me, and my heart is gladdened at the very thought of him.'

My father told us again how those few simple words from the lips of an old man of one hundered and five made such an impression on him that it never dimmed. It was as if he had listened to someone above ordinary mortals, a being who was no longer of this world, who had already 'entered into eternal life'. That was the very expression my father used.

They then talked about what the old man had witnessed during the reigns of Henry IV, Louis XIII, and that of Louis XIV which was then on the decline. My father was especially struck by his comment that the people realised what they had lost only after Henry's death, and that they had grumbled about him during his life.

My father used to quote these remarks of his, 'From the time of my birth, the ways of restraining the people have been gradually refined and their daily lives made more difficult by a hundred and one minor restrictions. As if frosts, hailstorms and fires weren't trouble enough, man has to add to them. But as the law is refined and even over-refined, wrong-doers become more ingenious in their methods of evading it, and from one refinement to another one reaches the point where the ruler and his subjects are just as clever as each other; unless, ultimately, they come face to face and state plainly to each other – 'That's what I want, for good or ill', or 'I won't have that, right or wrong' – and all bonds between them are broken. Wouldn't it be better to act in a straightforward manner? Are the minister and the magistrate to be counted more than their fellow men? Are the subject and the rogue to be counted less? If you think up one cunning trick, I can think up another, and only the honest man will suffer. It's a case of diamond cut diamond. The government should set an example of openness, rectitude, and loyalty. And if it fails to do so, priests, masses, vespers, sermons, salvation will count for nothing.'

'How lucky you are, father Brasdargent, to have seen so much and to remember it all.' 'Oh, my child, don't envy me my fate or my old age. Forty years ago now, I lost my last childhood friend, and I am like a stranger in the community and in my own family too. My grandchildren think I'm from another world. No one considers himself my peer, my friend, my companion. It's a curse to live too long. Just imagine, each new year for the past twenty-five to thirty years I thought would be my last. I no longer experience the hope which fills a young man's future with such promise, and which still brings comfort to a man in his middle years. I have exhausted the feelings that a father has for his children and the delights of having grandchildren. As I witness the birth of a fifth generation, nature no longer seems to want me to share such experiences. My grandchildren are like strangers to me, and I realise that they, in turn, have no affection for me. On the contrary, they are frightened and run away. That is the real truth, my friend, rather than all those fine phrases from clever town-dwellers, for whom everything is wonderful when they have a pen in their hand.'

One cannot dispute such sensible opinions, and, even though his final remarks are not very encouraging, his first point about the refinement of administrative practices is most illuminating. I don't recall any one else having made it, despite the fact that we experience daily the fatal consequences of these practices.

Once the wheat had been sown, Edmond returned to lawyer Rétif's and took up again his quiet tasks as if he had never left them. Besides Rétif's two sons, a cousin called Daiguesmortes was living with him (my father was only a second cousin). He was a young man of great promise, whose mind and precocious talents endeared him so much to the honest lawyer that he was afraid Edmond would become jealous. One day, he called him into the garden and after a few friendly exchanges said to him 'Edmond, I am pleased with you. You work as hard as you can, and if you have any failings they stem from lack of ability, and you cannot be blamed for that. I like you, my boy, because you are so well-behaved, and if I talk frankly with you, it's because we Rétifs are naturally more open than other folk in Burgundy. You must have noticed my fondness and indulgence towards Daiguesmortes. He is my first cousin, the son of an aunt who acted as a mother to me, but that is not all. He is extremely intelligent, and I intend to do everything in my power to develop his natural ability, convinced as I am he will make a name for himself and bring fame to us all. That's enough about him. As far as you are concerned, it would be a waste of time and effort to treat you in the same manner. He has a good mind, but, to put it bluntly, you do not. Someone else in my place might flatter you, but I'll tell you the truth. You mustn't feel resentful, however, for the way nature has treated you. That's all I have to say. If, on the other hand, I were a creator of men, a theanthropist as the Greeks call it, I know which I would make more of, and it wouldn't be Daiguesmortes. As I told you a moment ago, he is my first cousin and is closer to me than you, but you bear the same name as me and in that respect you are his equal. Go now, cousin, go back to your work and remember that I shall always be your friend. You might one day be a greater credit to me, because I have my doubts about clever people and could give you several examples, if I wanted to.'

My father repeated this conversation to us himself and took pleasure in emphasising the passages which were least favourable to him. Cleverness was an unnecessary attribute in such a

worthy man, as he had so many solid qualities which truly
ennoble mankind. We shall never know what Daiguesmortes
might have achieved, as he died when he was nineteen.

The following spring Edmond returned to his father and
found everything in a much better state than the first time.
That is because he had trained a ploughboy, who was a
relative of ours, during the previous half-year. This excellent
peasant, whose nickname was 'Touslesjours', was a Rétif (my
father often told us that everyone of this name, whether from
Anjou, Burgundy or Dauphiné, was of the same stock). I have
already explained the origin of this nickname in the first
volume of *L'Ecole des péres*, but, since this useful book is so
little known, doubtless because I have been unable to publicise
it enough, I shall tell it again here.

The young lad, who could only have been nine years old at
the time, was at catechism. The older boys and girls had
answered the priest's question 'How often must you forgive
your neighbour?' Some saying 'seventy times seven', as in the
Gospel, others 'as often as one can'. When the priest came to
the little boy, he replied 'You should forgive them every day.'

'You are right, my child', said the priest, patting his cheek.
'You have given the best answer. Were our neighbour to do
us harm every day, we should forgive him every day.'

The word 'everyday' was not forgotten. It became the
boy's nickname, and he was always proud of it, as one can
discover in the first volume of the work to which I have
referred.

Edmond was very pleased with what young Touslesjours
had done, and they became close friends. The help which he
received meant that he had time for rest, and he spent these
moments of leisure reading the Holy Scriptures, which is so
valuable for the improvement of the human heart.

There was in his father's house a complete Bible which,
because somewhat gallic in its expression, conveyed in a
simpler and more appealing way those excellent truths which
are contained in this, the oldest of books. Edmond, who was
so upright, drew from it the splendid philosophy of life which
was to bring him distinction one day. He was inspired by the
sublime and patriarchal values which it contained, and discovered in Leviticus, Numbers and above all in Deuteronomy

the basis of sound judgement and the source of all laws. When he came to the books of Wisdom, he read them with wonder, and learned the principles of good stewardship, which he respected already, and the true conduct between husband and wife. Finally, he learned from his reading that marriage is the one proper condition for man and that, unless he suffers from some physical disability, he should consider it a crime to accept any other. He also read the prophets, but never revealed his thoughts about them, because such strong emotion scarcely appealed to a judicious mind such as his. From the New Testament he only ever chose for family readings the Gospel of St. Mathew, the Acts of the Apostles and the Epistles of St. John. He never explained his reasons to us, and I can offer none myself. But the book he admired more than all the others and the one to which he returned constantly was Genesis. For him, the hero of the book was Abraham, but he extended his respect for the patriarchal figurehead to those of his descendants who are usually so reviled. He often attributed to them touching human qualities and even accorded them some respect.

Edmond did not return to lawyer Rétif's at Noyers at the end of that half year. His parents wanted him to see the capital, and so he left for Paris on November 11th, 1712, where he was to be a clerk to a magistrate in the law courts called Molé.

This was an entirely new experience for Edmond, but it did not change him. Although he had a lively temperament, the respect which he had for his mother extended to the whole of the opposite sex, and this preserved him from libertinism. What is more, he was a hard-working fellow, and the best antidote to vices of all kinds is to keep oneself fully occupied.

I must, however, relate one little adventure he had on his journey.

Because he was strong and healthy, Edmond scorned the idea of travelling by stage coach. And so, carrying his bundle, which included a fresh suit of clothes, two jackets, two pairs of breeches, eight shirts, several pairs of stockings, all wrapped up in a goatskin to protect it from the rain, he set out on foot and covered eighteen leagues each day. He could

easily have done more if it had only been one day's walk, but
it took at least three. On the last day, when he was just five
leagues from Paris, a white-haired old man, carrying a very
heavy basket, approached him. They walked along together
for a while and Edmond, who had quickened his pace in
order to arrive in good time, had to go very slowly.

'How lucky you are, young man', the old man said to him.
'Your bundle is as light as a feather to you and yet I'll wager
it's heavier than mine. But as well as my basket, I'm bearing
the burden of my seventy years. I shall have to let you go on
alone.'

Moved by what the old man said, Edmond replied, 'If you
wish, I will relieve you for a few leagues, as the weight of your
basket added to my bundle will hardly burden me, and I don't
want to be deprived of the honour of your company and of
your agreeable and entertaining conversation.'

Indeed, the old man, who came from Lyons and who
roamed far and wide in order to trade, had delighted Edmond
with his conversation. At first he pretended that he could not
accept the offer, but, as he had wanted to make the very same
proposition himself, he accepted. And so they reached Villejuif
together where the old man offered him some refreshment. But
young Edmond, who did not drink wine and who was in a
hurry to reach Paris, begged him to wait until they reached
their destination.

'But you must be tired.'

'I would even carry you as well as your basket if you were
unable to walk.'

The old man was a little uneasy, finding Edmond such a
willing lad, but he replied.

'I trust you as if you were my own son. I've got some
business to attend to here. You can leave me the basket, but, if
you are agreeable, I will put the heaviest things in your bundle.'

Edmond, who was innocence itself, willingly agreed. The
old man then did what he wanted and sewed up the goatskin
again with coarse thread. Edmond put it on his back so that he
could continue his journey.

'If I don't catch you up before you reach Paris, wait for me
here', the old man said, giving him the address of an inn in the
rue Mouffetard where he was known.

Edmond reached the tollgate alone and was asked what he was carrying.

'Only my bundle with a change of clothes and my under-clothes', he replied.

The men half opened the goatskin and, as it appeared that he had told them the truth, they didn't search it more thoroughly. Moreover, it is well known that the customs men only look closely at the people they suspect or at those who have been given away. An innocent young lad, whose face radiated honesty, aroused no suspicion. He was allowed through, and he went and waited for the old man so as to give him his things.

But the old man had no intention of catching him up, or of entering Paris at the same gate, or of meeting him at the appointed inn. He went through the gate St. Bernard, where even his clothing was searched. Then he was followed, because he was well-known for his tricks, and none believed that he would have come in empty-handed. He made his way to a street some distance from the one where he had arranged to meet Edmond, and straightway sent a young boy to Edmond who took him to someone else, with whom he was to leave the goods, before leading him back to the old man.

As soon as he entered, the old man hugged him, thanked him profusely and made a great fuss of him. Edmond was suprised at such a show of affection and embarrassed at the offer of a louis d'or which accompanied it. He thanked him, saying that he was happy to have been of service to an honest man and could not accept such a reward. He would, however, be grateful if he could kindly arrange for him to be taken to the magistrate's house where he was expected. But the old man insisted that he take the louis, and, in an attempt to persuade him, told of the valuable service he had performed.

'You carried in for me goods worth more than a hundred thousand livres. I'm offering you very little in return and, in all conscience, I ought to give you more, but I have your address and you can be sure that I shall never forget such a good turn.'

Edmond realised at this point that the man was a smuggler and that the goods he had carried in for him must have been precious stones. He had a strong sense of duty towards the

king, who only levied taxes for the good of the State, and he
had never been willing to involve himself at home in any
fraudulent evasion of taxes on wine, salt or tobacco. And it
was with these principles in mind that he addressed the old
man in the following terms.

'Sir, I did you a service out of the kindness of my heart and I
do not regret it, but I am most distressed at having helped to
cheat the king of his taxes. To accept any reward would be to
involve myself in an action which I abhor. You can count on
my discretion. I shall not give you away. But I bid you
farewell. I would not drink a glass of water in your company.'

With that, he walked out, much to the astonishment of the
old man and of the people who lived there.

When magistrate Molé saw what a fine lad Edmond was
and that he combined the strength of a lion with the gentleness
of a girl, he gave him a variety of jobs to do to try him out,
with the intention of relying on him a great deal. Because of
his fundamental innocence, Edmond was unaware that he was
being tested, and it seemed quite natural to him to find gold
coins lying around in the house of a rich man. Being tidy by
nature, he picked them up and placed them in his master's
desk without saying a word to anyone. When he was alone
with the daughter of the house and her maid, he would answer
the first respectfully and the other obligingly, and then return
to his work, once he had done what they asked. The
magistrate was delighted to have such a treasure in his
household, who performed his tasks with great alacrity.
Besides which, Edmond's handwriting, which he had learnt in
his native village, had a distinctive, natural quality, and his
letters were so well formed that one could read it as easily as
print. He could turn his hand to anything and was only
ashamed of being unoccupied. In this respect, his attitude
reflected the ways of the community from which he came, and
he never changed. He was soon well liked by everyone in the
household, who showed their affection and expressed it as
well; yet he never took advantage of it. When he learned that
they had been putting him to the test, he was most surprised
but responded with a pleasant smile.

Such great merit had brought Edmond to the point at
which he might have made his fortune, and what you are

about to read perhaps reveals the young man in the most favourable light of all.

At the end of the year, the magistrate had come to know him extremely well and wanted him for a son-in-law. With his wife's agreement, he spoke to his daughter about the matter, but the young lady's heart already inclined elsewhere. Not daring, however, to divulge anything to her parents, she preserved a modest silence. From this moment, Edmond was looked upon as one of the family and enjoyed the freedom of the house. He became aware that Mlle Molé wanted to talk to him in private but, because he was naturally shy, he avoided her. Finally, one day, they found themselves alone together.

'I want to speak with you, Edmond, about something that is of the utmost importance to me', the young lady said. 'Will you promise to do me a favour?'

'Most willingly'.

'Whatever I ask?'

'Yes, whatever you ask.'

'You know of my father's plan?'

'He paid me the compliment of saying something to me about it. But I am unworthy of such a great favour.'

'No, sir, you would not be unworthy. It is I who do not deserve you, as I already love someone else. That surprises you, but I beg you, dear Edmond, do me a service. Promise me you will.'

'I promise.'

'Refuse my hand without saying a word about what I have told you.'

'That will be extremely hard, as I shall not be telling the truth. If it is what you wish, though, I will refuse your hand. But were my father to order me, we should be in a terrible predicament.'

'I have taken care of that. I got my maid to write him a letter which will come as an awful shock.'

'I give you my word that I will do everything in my power.'

The next day, the magistrate talked openly with Edmond, but he made it plain that he could no longer entertain the idea of marriage.

The magistrate was puzzled by Edmond's response to his

generous offer, knowing full well the slender resources of his clerk.

'I have always thought you sensible until now', he said, 'but what am I to make of a young man who turns down a pretty girl and fifty thousand écus? I love my daughter, who is my sole heir, and I want to ensure her happiness by marrying her, not to some effeminate young man, but to a solid husband, who will so love her that she will never feel envious nor seek her pleasures elsewhere. Tell me, don't you find her attractive?'

'Oh, she's a charming young lady, sir.'

'Yet you have given up all idea of marrying her?'

'I am not worthy of her.'

'Is that all it is? I'll write to your father then.'

'You are my master and I am deeply grateful to you for your kindness, but I cannot accept the honour you would do me.'

'Well sir, I shall not force you. I realise I have made a mistake. Some village wench must have turned your head. You can return to her whenever you please.'

The magistrate was extremely angry, as any kind-hearted person would be whose generosity met with ingratitude. He went straight to his wife and poured out all his resentment against Edmond. Young Rétif had always shown the same respect, devotion and eagerness in serving her, and she was no less surprised than her husband. But women are more astute than men, and she felt that a refusal in these circumstances was unusual.

'He's fallen for a village girl', said her husband.

'That's not the reason. No village girl could outrival our daughter after eighteen months. What is more, I have certain proof that he is fond of her.'

'Indeed. That's crystal clear.'

However, the rumour soon spread throughout the household that Edmond had been dismissed. Everyone was sad about it, and they all began to wonder what he could have done to have displeased his master. When Mlle Molé heard about it, she knew the reason. She had still not dared to confess her true feelings either to her mother or father, but she was so touched by Edmond's generous action that, once it

became clear to her during dinner one day that her father was
no longer favourably disposed towards young Rétif, she
decided to go to her parents after the meal. At the very
moment that they were discussing how they might draw the
truth out of her, she appeared before them, blushing. First she
embraced them and begged their forgiveness, and they in turn
asked what reason she could have for seeking it. Whereupon,
a little hesitantly, she cofessed that she had commanded
Edmond to refuse her hand and explained her motives. The
first thought which came to magistrate Molé, and which made
him especially happy, was that he no longer had any cause to
complain about his favourite servant.

'You were right, my dear wife. As for you, Mlle, you can
return to your room. I shall speak with you later.'

He then sent for Edmond and said, 'What is this, my friend?
You would have left my household in order to please a girl
who won't even consider you!'

'Sir, before agreeing to do as she bade me, I thought it over
all one night, and I came to the conclusion that it was more
important for Mlle your daughter than for your clerk to find
favour in your eyes. Those were my thoughts. For the rest, I
hold you in great esteem and would have loved Mlle Molé
dearly, had I been accepted. The only favour I ask of you, sir,
is that Mlle suffers no reproach on my account, for I should
feel that deeply. I also hope that you can grant her her heart's
desire, so that her happiness might equal mine. She is a
charming person who deserves to be happy.'

'Poor fellow,' said magistrate Molé, 'he would have
sacrificed himself. You make me doubly regretful that I shall
not have you as my son-in-law. I shall, however, heed your
advice, and you will not lose by it.'

At this point in my study I will, as I promised, reveal
Edmond's character in its most favourable light, having set
the scene with what I have just told you. Mlle Molé married
the man she loved, who was a young lawyer and a suitable
match. But she was unhappy, and I shall return to that a little
later.

During the wedding celebrations for his daughter, M. Molé
talked of Edmond to one of friends, a rich silk merchant called
M. Pombelins, who owned the shop which still stands at the

corner of the rue Traversière and the rue St-Honoré, a little
below the rue Quinze-Vingts. He made no secret of the events
I have just related, and dwelt at length on all Edmond's
qualities. M. Pombelins was greatly impressed by what he
heard, as he had two charming daughters. The elder one
especially was a most accomplished young lady. Her father
cherished her dearly, and his only fear was that he might fail
her by arranging an unsuitable marriage. Sometimes, when a
friend spoke to him about it, he repeated these lines of
Euripides, with tears in his eyes.

'The wedding day is joyful, but who can express the anguish
of a father who hands the daughter he has raised with loving
care to an unknown party.'

It worried M. Pombelins above all that the beautiful Rose
was proud and haughty, and that cruel husbands take pleasure
in humiliating such women to the same extent they suffered in
winning them.

His friend's disclosures had given this kindly man something
to think about, and he resolved to question young Edmond for
himself and to decide what course of action he would take in the
light of his reactions.

There was no opportunity for a meeting during the wedding
celebrations, as Edmond alone was responsible during the
festivities for M. Molé's affairs and had to see that nothing was
delayed. He did his own work and that of his friends as well.
Once things had returned to normal, however, he had a little
free time, and M. Molé was able to tell him how M. Pombelins
had come to admire him and how much he wanted to meet
him. As a pretext, he suggested that the merchant wanted him
to help his daughters with their arithmetic. It was enough to
suggest something useful to Edmond for him to seek to do it
without delay. And so he went to M. Pombelins. He admitted
subsequently that he was dazzled by Rose's beauty and that he
had never before seen anyone so lovely. She was a charming
girl, with a most attractive face and a figure to match, and her
physical attributes were allied to qualities of heart and mind.
The firmness of Edmond's resolve could not withstand such
excellence. She was his first and only passion, for, on the two
previous occasions, he had not given way to his feelings. He
took care, even on this occasion, not to allow his amorous

inclinations to develop before he had learnt whether his suit would be acceptable to the girl's parents. For three whole months, he fulfilled his obligations towards their father without betraying his feelings in any way. His punctuality alone suggested that he enjoyed visiting the house.

At first, the progress of the two pupils was rapid. They understood everything, and, after a few days, it seemed to him that there was not much more he could teach them. Thus, he was somewhat surprised when they kept getting stuck at the same point. But he blamed himself and redoubled his efforts.

Eugénie, the younger of the two sisters, was as pretty as Rose was beautiful, and as lively and frivolous as the other was sober and serious. She had noticed her father's goodwill towards young Rétif and had overheard his complimentary remarks to his wife about him. She was unaware of her parents' intentions, but presumed it would not displease them if she behaved kindly towards Edmond.

One day, when he was giving her a lesson, the young minx said to him, laughing.

'Come now, don't bother yourself so. I know as well as you how to work this one out, and a shorter way. As we are alone, let us have a little talk.'

Edmond was suprised at the way she spoke and did not know what to say in reply. But she went on.

'I am certain that Mama and Papa are very fond of you, and would not refuse you either my sister's hand or my own. Rose is more beautiful and would undoubtedly win your favour if she so wished. I do not want to fall in love until she has made her feelings known. Make her decide, and if she turns you down, count on me. I am honest with you because I know you are too. Tell me now what you think . . . No, I won't press you to admit that you like me better than my sister', she added, seeing how embarrassed Edmond was. 'I am only trying to soften the blow, if she should happen to refuse you, and to tell you that you do have a second-best, who is not altogether unattractive. I realise I am speaking a little more frankly than country girls would, but you can rest assured that I am not in love with you, not at all. I would certainly be well contented were you to become my husband, as I am sure that any woman would have a happy, tranquil life with such a reasonable and steady young man, who has none of the faults of our Parisian admirers, whom I really cannot bear, M. Edmond. There, that is what I so wanted you to know.'

At that moment, her sister Rose entered the room, and when she had had her lesson, he withdrew.

Once the two girls were alone, Eugénie, who had come to realise that, in his heart, Edmond preferred her elder sister, resolved to discover Rose's feelings, in order to know her own position.

'Dearest Rose', she began, 'we are as close friends as we are sisters. Please tell me truthfully if you would accept M. Rétif as your husband, were Mama and Papa to propose it? I have my reasons for asking this question, which I want you to answer honestly. There is no need for blushes. You need not be afraid of me. Come now, tell me.'

'Really', replied Rose, 'what a strange matter to concern yourself with all of a sudden!'

'I tell you, I have my reasons for asking. What do you think of our tutor?'

'He is unlike any other young man I have ever met.'

'So you have no objections to him?'

'I don't bother my head with such thoughts.'

'Well, I bother about them. Marriage is an honourable estate, and Mama is not in the least ashamed of having married Papa. Moreover, one ought to give a great deal of thought to the matter, as one pledges oneself for life.'

'Truly, Eugénie, I see that we were quite wrong to treat you as a scatter-brain. I had not imagined you capable of such sound reasoning. Well, dear sister, since you press me, if father and mother wished it, I would consider it. Not that I am in love with the young man in question, but his behaviour at least does not set me against the idea of marriage.'

'I have told him the very same thing. You see, we think alike on this.'

'Told whom?'

'Edmond. I was touched by his shyness, and as I feared that you might refuse him and that, being so shy, a refusal might have . . . I told him that even if you refused him, I would not do so. In that way I hoped to show that I respected him, and to give him a little more confidence.'

'What, sister, you've . . .!'

'No harm has been done. You like him. Someone else will be found for me. Tomorrow I shall tell him that you accept him.'

'Take care, sister. That is not how these things are done.'

'Very well, I shall say nothing. But if you are to marry first, I might well have to wait until I'm thirty. He will not speak first, and you will say nothing. On the contrary, knowing you, you will become even more aloof.'

'It is for our parents . . .'

'Yes, you are quite right. I will talk to Papa straight away.'

And with that the impetuous young Eugénie ran off singing, paying no heed to his sister, who tried to restrain her.

Rose's parents were delighted to learn of their daughter's feelings, but they took care to respect her genuine embarrassment and even permitted her to deny everything to her sister. However, that same evening, M. Pombelins visited M. Molé to let him know that their plans were likely to succeed.

'It is simply a question now', he added, 'of making sure that our expectations of the young man's present conduct are well founded.'

'I will answer for him', said Magistrate Molé, 'but you may put him to whatever test you will, with my backing. I give you my word of honour that I will not give you away.'

The next day, M. Pombelins greeted young Rétif even more warmly than usual, and for the first time this excellent father told him of his intentions, as far as the marriage of his daughters was concerned.

'My friend', he said, 'since nature bestowed on me the role of father, I have done everything in my power to fulfil my duty. Whilst my children were small and needed only the attention of their mother, I looked to my business affairs, so that they would never want for anything. By God's grace, I have been successful, and the two surviving daughters of my six children will receive generous dowries. Now that they have grown up, I have other responsibilities towards them. I have for a long time studied the workings of the human heart on their behalf, and especially the make-up and character of those who live in town. That was the most important aspect of my study, as my daughters have grown up in the city and will, of course, settle there.

'In the course of my study, I have made the unhappy discovery that a man born in the town is never as reliable as one born in the country. He is useless when compared with the latter, despite all the attention he receives. In order to reform him and make him what he should be, a man, one would have to transplant him, to the countryside and bring him up there from birth until he was fifteen to twenty, depending on whether he was forward or backward. People look for reasons for the decline of the Romans and for the collapse of their Republic, but it was entirely due to the degeneration and the increasingly effeminate ways of the Roman town-dwellers. So long as the young patricians worked on the land, they remained virtuous, and, as M. Molé remarked one day, the man who is free from all worries in the satisfaction of his daily needs spends his time stimulating artificial needs, such as lust, lechery and ambition, or all of them together. Another thing I have noticed, which has to do more with politics than with morals, is that the older our business houses become, the less active they are. I would even go as far as to say that their integrity and vigour decline as well. That is quite natural. As enterprise diminishes and the taste for luxury increases, some loss of integrity is inevitable. I came to the conclusion early on that a father, if he is wise, will see to it that his sons take up quite different occupations from his own, so that different ways of life are intermixed, just as races are intermixed to improve them. Furthermore, as far as any daughters he may have are concerned, he will reinvigorate the human race by giving them, as husbands, active and hard-working young men from the provinces, who are thrifty, strong, and healthy in mind and body, and without any weaknesses or eccentricities. And even if they bring nothing with them by way of a dowry, their good character and their industry will make up for it, as long as they are well chosen. I have seen this happen in families where the head of the household has shared my views; and today those families are thriving. But if fathers allow their sons to follow in their own footsteps, apathy sets in, and if they marry off their daughters to city-dwellers, they totally degenerate within three generations.

'People, of course, argue against me, claiming that the young man brought up in a town will be unable to find a wife. I wish I could propose an exchange, whereby young city-dwellers would marry country girls and Parisian girls would go to country lads, but unfortunately this is quite impractical. What would young Parisians find to do in the countryside? They would simple languish there. I know of two who married men from your region, and who have been unable to get used to the loneliness or to their husbands' ways, and have pined away. What is more, they are incapable of adapting themselves to country chores, and they cannot even run their household properly. Each person must do as he can, therefore, and I shall make suitable arrangements for my children, even though others cannot do the same. I should not, of course, discuss things so openly with anyone less modest than yourself, M. Rétif. I would much prefer my daughters to marry young men from the provinces and countrymen in particular, with no money, rather than Parisians who might have considerable wealth.'

M. Pombelins believed that he had explained things sufficiently clearly to Edmond. And in order that he might understand that it was the lovely Rose he was to marry, from that day on she alone had lessons with him. Eugénie was sent to spend some time with one of her aunts, called Mme de Varipon, who had just lost her husband and whose only son was away from home.

The two lovers were often alone together, yet Edmond did not reveal his feelings towards her for two whole months, even though they were very strong. Fortune had set them apart socially, and this made him timid. Besides which, a certain natural modesty prevented him from expressing them. He was, however, friendly and courteous towards Rose's mother and father and behaved respectfully towards her, paying her such fond attention that M. Pombelins was in no doubt as to his affection for her. Since he felt that he could count on this young man of modest means, he decided not to hurry things, preferring to watch the flames of passion grow in an upright and innocent heart. Nothing gave this keen observer of behaviour greater pleasure. Won over at last by Edmond's true worth, yet still enjoying a semblance of

freedom, the proud Rose was perfectly happy. Edmond was
so rapturously in love with this enchanting and beautiful girl
that his naturally soft voice became softer still. Every word,
even the most ordinary things, seemed to say 'I love you',
because of the way he said them, and because of the shy and
respectful look which accompanied them. A delightful inti-
macy, which might have been dangerous for others, grew up
between them. They began to smile knowingly at each other
when someone else was talking, and Edmond performed
those small services for his beloved, which are the prerogative
of one who is favoured. She would ask him trustingly and he
would obey her willingly and even eagerly.

Things had reached this stage when Eugénie returned
home. She watched the two lovers for a few days without
saying anything, and then confessed to her sister.

'Dear Rose, I am going to tell you a secret.'

'I shall be pleased to share it, dearest sister.'

'I also have a lover.'

'Also, dear sister.'

'Yes, it's cousin Varipon. He fondly declared his love to me
the day before I returned home. I haven't yet given him my
answer, but I think I can, now that you and M. Rétif are
betrothed. I am free to take back the promise I made him.'

'How remarkably perceptive you are, little sister.'

'Is that so, elder sister? It's quite alright, I am happy about
it. Father told me yesterday that he thought our cousin well
brought-up and not at all like a Parisian. So my feelings will
not displease him, and we can both be happy, can't we?'

Rose blushed and did not reply. Just then, Edmond came into
the room, for the cunning young Eugénie had taken care not
to bring up the subject with her sister until the very moment
at which he usually arrived at the house.

'Oh, you've come just at the right time', she said. 'You
remember what I once told you?'

'You have done me the honour of telling me a number of
things, Mlle.'

'Come now, stop pretending. I am referring to something
you surely haven't forgotten, in spite of your air of modesty.'

'No, Mlle, I haven't forgotten and I never shall.'

'Well, you can after today, you can, do you hear?'

'Is it my misfortune to have . . .?'

'No, it's not your misfortune', she replied, imitating him, 'it's your good fortune that you no longer need my generosity. Look at the two of you! One would think I was talking of something you knew nothing about.'

'For my part, I am ignorant of it, Mlle.'

'Well, that's splendid, my return will at least have served some useful purpose.'

'My sister has become no more sensible, Monsieur, for having stayed so long with the most rational and the most sorrowful woman in Paris.'

'I'll wager that you haven't yet said you love each other. Come now, do it in front of me, as you both know it's true.'

Edmond's heart thrilled with joy, but Rose, well she just looked the perfect Rose at that moment.

'Really, Eugénie! You know that what you're saying is very foolish. I can't imagine what M. Edmond will think of you.'

'Oh, I know quite well what he thinks when he hears someone talking plainly, who only wants to help him and spare him embarrassment. I am certain that, after you, he loves me dearly.'

At this, Edmond could no longer restrain himself and tears of joy rolled down his cheeks.

'How well you have spoken, Mlle', he exclaimed. 'Goodness, what an adorable family you are, and how happy you make me with all your favours. I hold M. Pombelins in the same esteem as my father. He is the wisest and most respectable of men, and I cannot tell you how much I love and revere him. Mme Pombelins is for me the living image of Anne Simon, and if you knew her Mlles, you would realise what a compliment I pay your mother. As for you, their dearest daughters, all I can say is that you are treasures of your sex. May heaven grant you the happiness you deserve, and, should I have any part in it, to the one I pledge my fondest and most respectful affection and to the other the surest and strongest friendship, so that she may never regret her kindness to me.'

'What a show of feeling', cried Eugénie. 'It is somewhat novel or perhaps a little old-fashioned, but, for my part, I am quite satisfied with it. Are you, Mlle?'

'Monsieur is well-mannered and answers your frivolities

with discretion, sister', Rose replied, blushing.

'Now you have given me your answer too', said Eugénie, 'and you have both declared your love. Proclaim it aloud therefore, so that your younger sister may learn from what she hears. Say pretty things to each other, but not mere trifles. You both have the wit for it.'

'I would only have to listen to my heart, Mlle', Edmond replied, 'in order to tell your sister all the things . . . But I prefer to keep them modestly to myself, as a pleasure which offended modesty would be no pleasure at all for me.'

'Oh Rose, you have found the lover who will truly satisfy your kind, proud heart.'

Turning to Rose, Edmond then said, 'If you will only grant me the liberty, I shall hope to show by my conduct towards you, rather than by what I could say, my strong and lasting feelings. Just one encouraging glance is all the encouragement I ask.'

Rose lowered her eyes without replying.

'That is the very least he could have asked for', said Eugénie.

Then Rose looked up at him with shining eyes and stretching her hand towards him, said, 'My father, whom I love and respect as much as you respect yours, has chosen you. If he is willing to serve as intermediary, he will tell you of my feelings.'

At that moment, M. and Mme Pombelins came in to see their children. They told Edmond of their intentions and offered him Rose's hand in marriage. When Edmond had expressed his gratitude, M. Pombelins added.

'Write to your father. I await only his consent.'

Edmond had been in the capital two and half years and was about twenty. Not for a single moment did he imagine that the proposal of such a favourable match would meet with any hesitation on his parents' part. He was mistaken, however. But his behaviour in this matter reveals above all the splendid example of filial obedience he set.

His father, Pierre, had never left his native province, and he held the strangest views about the capital. Unfortunately, these views had been reinforced by the letter which Mlle Molé had written, asking him not to consent to the marriage which had been proposed between herself and Edmond. And on this particular subject he did not consult lawyer Rétif, who was a friend of M. Molé's.

As soon as Edmond's letter reached Nitri, together with one from the magistrate, his employer, they imagined him doomed, deceived, the victim of some shameful and dishonourable plan. Pierre, believing his son less obedient and already corrupted, decided upon a course of action which he felt sure would make him return home at once. It was certainly effective, but altogether unnecessary, and it was almost self-defeating. For, when Edmond received the message requesting him to return home to his dying father's bedside, he fainted. As a result, he missed one ferry, and had to delay his departure to the next one. No one wanted him to leave until a letter had been sent to lawyer Rétif and a reply received. Furthermore, magistrate Molé, whose daughter had confessed about her letter once she was married, suspected something. But, in the circumstances, Edmond would hear of no further delay. And so, utterly dejected, he set out, overwhelmed by M. Pombelins's expression of friendship, and sadly missed by Rose. He was told, however, that he could write to her and that she would be expected to reply.

BOOK 2

When he reached Auxerre Edmond found Touslesjours there, who had come to meet him on horseback.

'How is my father?' he asked anxiously, as he embraced his friend.

'Quite well, quite well', replied the young man, who knew nothing of the secret.

'He's out of danger! What a relief!'

'Out of danger! He's not been ill!'

Edmond was overjoyed at this happy news, and, though he reflected sadly on the reasons for his recall, he swore to us that his only feeling was one of joy. Having disembarked from the river ferry, he set out without a moment's delay.

On the journey, he and Touslesjours talked only of the state of the farm and the work that was being done. When they had gone about four leagues and were close to Provenchère wood, where the road forks, Touslesjours, who was a little ahead of Edmond, turned right.

'That's not the way to Nitri'. Edmond called out.

'I know that, but your father is waiting for you at Saci, at his friend M. Dondaine's.'

This M. Dondaine was a wealthy inhabitant of Saci, a man of great good sense, industrious, thrifty, shrewd, and who owed the fortune he had acquired to his own hard work and intelligence. Worthy and respectable ways of amassing wealth! But he was a hard man with an unpleasant face, whose strength was legendary in his own neighbourhood, where they are like cart-horses. Thomas Dondaine's faults were not so much his own as those of the region from which he came. Coarseness and toughness are innate characteristics and are caused by two things, the heavy air they breathe, as the village is situated in a valley which is marshy for three quarters of the year, and the sudden change they experience when they set out to work in their vineyards and their fields on the hillsides.

41

There, the air is so sharp and keen that the villagers of Saci usually eat more than twice as much bread as the men from the surrounding villages. One can see, therefore, why these people are not very attractive. However, they have so many other good qualities, that, when one gets to know them, one cannot help admiring them and having a certain affection for them, as they are perhaps the most hard-working people in the world.

Edmond knew Thomas Dondaine and he did not like him. He was also aware that he had three daughters. His own father, who was in fact pefectly well, was with Thomas Dondaine, waiting for him to arrive. His heart filled with sadness. He feared that something terrible was about to happen. When he reached the bleak and barren landscape of Saci, the sight of the parched and stony fields and the guttural and inarticulate shouts of the lumbering husbandmen, who were struggling against nature and striving to scratch a living, made him feel more sorrowful and downcast than he had ever been in his whole life.

By the time he arrived in Saci, he was parched with thirst and already feeling the effects of the climate on his appetite. Only love or grief could possibly have assuaged it in such a place.

As he entered the village, there was a hemp-field in which three thickset, mannish girls were gathering the crop. Edmond was astonished at their industry and effort and at their strength in carrying the bundles of hemp. He remarked to Touslesjours 'They aren't very pretty, but they will make good wives.'

Edmond found his father waiting at Thomas Dondaine's. After three years absence he was greeted with the customary severity.

'You've kept me waiting, my son.'

'The news of your illness alarmed me, dear father.'

'I trust there is no other reason.'

'That was reason enough, and I thank God that I find you in good health.'

'And in good spirits', added Thomas Dondaine. 'But, my friend, this son of yours looks too much of a dandy to work our stony land.'

'We'll soon change all that.'

It is impossible to convey the coarseness of Thomas Dondaine's speech. The dialect of this district matches the harshness of the landscape and the physical features of the people. It is dull, coarse and incoherent, whereas the speech of Nitri people is soft and musical, which can be explained by the fact that they pronounce their consonants as in Greek, that each word is spoken with a slight, soft accent, and that they speak an almost pure French. The village is situated on a plateau above the hills of Saci where the air, undisturbed by small valleys, is pure without being keen.

'I sent for you in order to settle your marriage, my son. Instead of some faithless and corrupt coquette from the town, I've found you an upright girl who will be a devoted wife. You might well have fancied a pretty little dressed-up creature, but you can put thoughts like that out of your head. If you raise the slightest objection, I shall not hesitate to lay my curse on you.'

'I haven't enquired how my mother is', replied Edmond, trembling.

'Your first concern is to obey me. As for your mother, she is well and counts on your obedience to our will. I'm saying all this because you haven't yet met the girl. I've chosen her for you, with the agreement of my friend, who has done me the honour of accepting you as his son-in-law before he knew whether you'd be suitable.'

'That's well spoken', replied Thomas. He then turned to his wife and said 'Go and fetch your girls from the hemp-field and tell them to come at once. The lad is hot and must be hungry and even thirstier.'

He wanted to pour Edmond a glass of wine, but this young lad from Burgundy had never drunk it, as was the custom in those days. Neither young people nor women drank wine, apart, that is, from mothers over forty who just coloured their water with a drop. Before that, even when they were pregnant, they never touched it. Edmond thanked him.

'Give him some milk', his father said, 'he prefers it to wine.'

As Edmond finished drinking, Thomas Dondaine's three daughters came in with their mother. Marie, the eldest, was the least attractive, but her appearance suggested a kindly

disposition. What a change for Edmond! Her father introduced him to Marie as the man she would be marrying in
three days time, the arrangements have already been made.
The girl blushed out of modesty, and, although her future
husband was to her liking, she said to her father:

'Dear father, that is rather soon. Not that I have any
objections against such a sensible young man, whom everyone admires. But we ought to get to know each other, and he,
at least, should discover whether I am suitable. Obedience
forbids any hesitation on a daughter's part, once her father has
spoken, but it is rather different for a man, I think.'

A simple command to be quiet, firmly spoken by Thomas,
was the only reply she received.

'You understand our wishes?' Pierre asked his son.

'Yes father.'

'I want no objections.'

'Father, I would be an utter wretch and wholly unworthy
of being a parent myself one day, were I to oppose your will.
On an occasion such as this, your authority as a father is
supreme. In life as in death, I will obey you and my mother,
whom I regard highly. Give your command, and trouble
yourself no more about it, for it is unthinkable that I should
disobey you.'

'Those are fine words, my son', said Pierre, with a slight
smile. 'One at least learns how to give a courteous answer in
town, even if one's deeds cause some displeasure.'

They sat down to eat. After dinner, father and son set out
together for Nitri. Once they were out of the village, Pierre
rode alongside his son, which was unusual.

'My son', he said, 'you are about to enter upon a new life.
As a result of your obedience in accepting it, you will be
blessed by God and praised by men. One day, you can expect
your children to look up to you, as you looked up to your
own father.'

Never before had Pierre spoken so gently to his son, and
Edmond was moved to tears as he grasped his father's hand
and said:

'Father, I have made a great sacrifice for you.'

'Indeed. You don't mean that. Mere hussies! They'd be-
witched you.'

'Oh father, if only you knew her, if you knew her worthy father.'

'Let's not mention those people', said Pierre, in a friendly and familiar tone, which he had never before adopted with Edmond.

I shall obey you father, were it to be the death of me.'

'I don't like that mournful tone of voice', retorted Pierre, with a frown. 'Don't let me hear it again.'

After a few moments silence, he seemed to soften and went on:

'Dear Edmond, my dear son, you are about to marry. Don't behave as I have done. I have set a bad example, but I will make amends, if God lets me live a little longer. I have almost concluded a business transaction with the monks of Molême in which you will have a half share. It will bring some comfort to your mother, which is what she deserves from me at least. Once you are married, you will be my friend and equal. Only our closer friendship and a greater forbearance we shall show each other will reveal that we are still father and son.'

At these kind words, Edmond, choking with emotion, jumped from his horse and kissed his father's feet. He, in turn, touched by his son's gesture, got down and, throwing his arms around his neck, said:

'You are my one and only son and I have always loved you. I want you to live in the country as a good family man, rather than as a bourgeois in town. It is a more patriarchal way of life.'

Had it not been for Rose, how happy Edmond would have been at this moment to rediscover beneath the hardest of taskmasters the kindest of fathers.

They walked on together, leading their horses by the rein, whilst Touslesjours went ahead to announce their arrival to Anne Simon.

'What would have become of you in town? You'd have been a good citizen, I agree, but your children would have grown up far from here, which is our birthplace. They would have been swallowed up in the horde of city-dwellers and would soon have forgotten their roots. You know this yourself. Lawyer Rétif told me he'd said something to you about it. We are all sons of Adam, I know, but we should still

be proud of our own stock. And though the name Rétif is
only a nickname, it is so old that our real name has been
forgotten, especially since those terrible wars of religion in
which we were dispossessed. But it's a consolation to me, as it
will be to you one day, to return to these parts where our
family is so loved and respected. Villèrs, Aigremont, Courtenai, whenever I see you again, I feel a lump in my throat. Let
us never leave our birthplace nor settle in some large town.
Let us renew constantly and enjoy forever our attachment and
our esteem for our ancestors. On your mother's side, you are
related to one of the best families in the province. That is why
I chose her. And she chose me because of the name to which
my worthy and respected father had brought such distinction.
You know what he was called, the 'just man', what a name!
One of our relations inherited it, and it has never gone out of
the family. Such titles are worth more than those we have
lost, my son, a hundred times more. To be truthful, I have no
time for all those old parchment scrolls, which are more often
acquired as a consequence of intrigue rather than as a reward
for good deeds one's ancestors might have done. How many
nobles there are whose forefathers were greedy oppressors! I
am talking of the old nobility. As for the modern nobility, tax
collectors who buy . . . If they are useful to the State because
of the money they hand over, all well and good. But they buy
cheaply what ought to be the reward for all kinds of heroism.
My son, today we belong to the common people and I am
thankful for that. The commoner is the best of men. He
pays taxes, works, sows crops, harvests them, trades, builds,
manufactures. The privilege of contributing nothing is a
dubious privilege. Let us not regret it. You have seen the
gentlemen huntsmen of La Puisaie in their gaiters and hob-
nailed boots, wearing rusty old swords and dying of hunger,
but blushing at the thought of work. Would you want to be in
their position?'

'No father, the middle class, that precious class, so prized
by good kings, is the one in which I want to live and die. Dear
father, you and the worthy M. Pombelins share the same
opinions.'

'Yes, but he wanted to set you up in town. Tell me, what
would have happened to our descendants once they'd become

part of the town riff-raff? I say again, let us remain here. Everything around us reminds us of our family. Everything will keep you mindful of our honour, and that can sometimes be useful. Good M. Pombelins was your worst enemy.'

'Dear father, I will obey you. But say nothing against a man whom you would like, if you knew him. As a father, I beg you, say nothing against a girl . . . Oh how I wish she were a fourth sister to me at this moment.'

He began to shed tears as he uttered these words. And Pierre, having seemingly dropped his naturally haughty tone after his last remarks, said to his son:

'Sensibility is the mark of a generous soul. You weep, but you are obedient. I am no tyrant. I have only praise for you. But your future happiness, in this world and the next, is dependent upon this important event. Your obedience will ensure that you have good children.'

And then, as if inspired, and aware that his life was drawing to a close, he spoke forcefully to his son, 'Edme, cursed is the son or daughter who does not respect his father, and blessed are the son and daughter who are obedient, depite what they might feel in their hearts. Heaven will bless them. Whatever sorrow marriage may bring will appear as nothing if they can say to themselves in all conscience 'Lord, I have been obedient. I have obeyed you in obeying my father, who is the image of your glory on earth.' My dear son, I give you my blessing. It is the heartfelt expression of my joy and my contentment. And in giving it, I entrust to your care your dear mother and your sisters, when I am gone. Bear with Catherine, who is difficult, and cherish Madelon, who is kindness itself. I fear for Marion, as she is frivolous and a scatter-brain. You will have to curb her. I confer my authority upon you as my right-hand man during my lifetime and as my successor after my death. As for the wrongs I have done your mother, whose patience I have sorely tried, you must take them upon yourself. Settle my debts and repay her with respect and tenderness for the unkindness and intolerance she has suffered at my hands. Oh Lord, I have done wrong, but here is my son. May what he does in my place be acceptable to you.'

'It is impossible to express' (my father often told us) 'what I felt in my heart as I listened to my father, who was so distant and so proud and who had become so affectionate. I was overwhelmed. I would have married the ugliest creature on earth. I would have worshipped her, if my father had so bidden me at that moment.'

Such were their spirits when they returned home, where Edmond was welcomed in his mother's arms. As I write this, the pen falls from my hand. Oh worthy woman! Trembling with emotion, her heart went out to him, but the strength drained from her limbs and she had to sit down. Her arms were outstretched; the tenderest of motherly endearments were on her lips, but she could not express them. There was so much she wanted to say, yet not one word was spoken. Happily, her tears flowed freely, bathing her worthy son as she clasped him to her. At last she spoke.

'Pierre, forgive me for being so overcome with emotion', she said to her husband, 'but he is my son and the image of his father.'

'And a worthy son', cried Pierre. 'Shower all your maternal affection upon the worthy lad, like the good mother you are. He will take my place with great distinction, when I am gone.'

Anne Simon was extremely surprised, hearing him speak in this unexpected manner. She gave her son her blessing and then, getting up quickly, she hastened to make her husband comfortable, as was her custom. 'I must not pay so much attention to my dear son that I forget his father', she said. 'Come now, daughters, take care of your brother. I have my duty to perform, which I shall yield to no one, not even to my own children.'

When the two men were refreshed, Pierre explained the rest of his plans to his son. Edme would go to live in Saci with his father-in-law, as that was a necessary part of their undertaking. He then told him about the land which Thomas Dondaine was expected to hand over, and he showed such good will as he explained everything, that Anne Simon, seated a little apart from them out of respect, listened with admiration to father and son alike, and wept with joy.

'In three days time, my son will achieve manhood', said Pierre, 'and we should both begin to show him the consideration he deserves.'

Only a mother could imagine the thrill Anne Simon felt at her husband's kindly remark. Only a mother who has a son could know its import and true meaning. But her sole response was a half-uttered cry of joy. At supper, however, this good woman seemed to serve her son and to address him with such respect, that she earned another compliment from her husband. He called her 'Sara, virtuous Sara', the highest praise a woman could be given.

Then Pierre said to his son, 'Agriculture is the noblest art practised by man. All others depend on it, and the riches which it provides are alone worthy of the name. Let us remain at the fountainhead of life, the purest of all springs. It is honourable to engage in an activity upon which all others depend. What is the merchant, if not our middleman? The artist and the artisan would not exist without us. Let us recognise our importance, my son, and be proud of it.'

Edmond felt elated that evening and was beside himself with joy at such family scenes, which he had not witnessed before. But when night came, in the quietness of his own heart, his thoughts were troubled. Love, that ruling passion which is more powerful in a noble soul where it is a virtue, assailed him in all its painful and disturbing force. The image of the lovely Rose Pombelins, the thought of her honourable and upright father, and the memory of so much kindness shown him by her family overwhelmed him with feelings of regret. He was on the edge of a double precipice; on the one side, the loss of the woman he loved, his life's happiness, an easy, agreeable, a glorious future even, and the possibility of making his fortune; on the other, disobedience to his father's command, which he contemplated only for a moment. Disobedience horrified him, was unthinkable, given Pierre's character and the upbringing his son had received. With trepidation and after a great struggle, Edmond forced himself to accept the alternative course of action. When I learned of these events from my worthy father's own mouth, his sorrow was undiminished, though forty years had passed.

More wearied by his inner struggles than by his journey, Edmond did not close his eyes the whole night long. He fell asleep at daybreak and got up a little later than usual. When he awoke, the whole household was in a state of agitation. He

inquired the reason. His father was seized with a violent fever.
He rushed to his bedside, and the first words his father spoke
were:

'My friend, if I should die, promise me that you will carry
out the plans I've made, without delay. It is my wish that you
should do so.'

'I swear I will, father.'

'May you be blessed, for you bring happiness to your dying
father's heart.'

'You, dying, father. God will not allow it.'

'My end is near . . .' forestalling his son's reply, he went
on, 'Go and see to everything and set my mind at rest. Your
mother and your sisters can take care of me well enough. Go
and see to things, my son. Play the man's part, for soon you
will be the only one.'

Compelled more by a forceful gesture than by his father's
words, Edmond withdrew, griefstricken. He was scrupu-
lously obedient, doing all the household jobs on a list which
his mother had given him. He saw his father again at
lunchtime. The fever seemed to have abated, but the patient
was short of breath, and as he was extremely opposed to
blood-letting, this remedy could not be applied. They were in
despair. Edmond gave him an account of what he had done,
but Pierre could scarcely reply and nodded his approval. He
was thirsty.

'Give me a drink, my son.'

Catherine rushed forward.

'No, I want my son. May God bless you, Edme, as I do. Be
like a father to the girls and give this good and honourable
woman your support, when I am gone.'

He drank thirstily. Edmond wept. Anne Simon let out a cry
of grief.

'A blood-letting', she said.

'No, no', he retorted, 'God will save me, if it is his will.'

'Father . . .', said Edmond.

'I hear you, my son. No, mother nature is my guide. I trust
in her alone. Go and see to things.'

Edmond left him. In the evening, he was a little better, but
exhausted. The next day, the fever became more and more
violent. His mind was confused. Any stranger was vigorously

pushed away, but he was always gentle to his wife and son. He recognised them even when he was delirious. On the third day, he regained his lucidity for a short while. He remembered that the marriage should have been celebrated that day and spoke to the priest, complaining that they had not complied with his wishes.

'Shall he marry at the same time as he buries his father?' the priest asked.

'Yes, yes, sir.'

They made ready to obey him and set out for Saci. But Pierre suffered a sudden change for the worse, and died at one in the afternoon, at the age of forty-two.

Edmond's first reaction was one of grief at such a great loss. His feelings were different from those which children usually have. Edmond had lost a father who was to him the living image of God. Never was grief so intense. His despair would have made the most unfeeling weep.

Thomas Dondaine arrived. He had not been informed of Pierre's death. When Edmond noticed him, he got up and ran to him.

'You alone are my father now', he said. 'You were my own father's choice; he gave me to you. I give you my word that I shall show the same repect and obedience as I showed him.'

Thomas, aware of the real inclination of Edmond's heart, believed the marriage would be called off. He had come with the intention of releasing him from his obligation, on the grounds that they could not now proceed with the proposed marriage. But he was so surprised and so moved by Edmond's gesture that he embraced him and said, 'And you shall not be my son-in-law, but my son. I will tell my daughter that her happiness is assured, as a respectful son will surely be a good husband. You have won her heart. May you both be blessed. You will be a consolation to me in my old age, and together we can mourn the loss of my friend. I shall leave now and return tomorrow with my daughter. I want her to be a mourner at the just man's funeral, to share your grief and tears, as if she were already his daughter-in-law.'

'Father, the worthy man wanted it to take place today', said Edmond.

'Let us hold it tomorrow', replied Thomas. 'Obedience is more important than propriety. If our two priests agree, I would like the body of our worthy Pierre to be the principal and most respected witness.'

That is how the marriage was celebrated, as the two priests consented, obeying the spirit rather than the letter of the law. Edmond, his head bowed, performed his duty. He married Marie Dondaine before the body of his venerated father, promising obedience to God. And he offered a fervent prayer that the author of his days might find eternal rest.

The priest who did not marry them preached a short sermon to his parishioners. 'My children', he said, 'a son has obeyed the wishes of his dead father.' He explained that it was out of respect for the deceased and on his orders that Edmond had celebrated his marriage in this extraordinary manner. Oh, if he could only have told them the whole story, as he knew it. But these admirable priests, the wise Pinard, priest of Nitri, and the good Pandevant, priest of Saci, were full of admiration and wept with compassion and grief.

After the wedding, the funeral ceremony was completed. Grief-stricken, Edmond walked behind his father's coffin, his eyes blurred with tears, not knowing where he was. Yet he held his bride by the hand and seemed to present her to his father and to say 'I have obeyed you; give me your blessing once more.'

As the body was lowered into the grave, the priest of Nitri, overcome with emotion, cried out in French 'Pierre, my friend, my companion, you have been obeyed! May your blessed soul rest in eternal peace! Amen!' And the whole congregation cried out several times, Amen. For Pierre was well liked because of his integrity and his resistance to any kind of solicitation. He would not accept gifts, and he settled more cases than he ever judged. His son followed his example.

The priest, as is the custom, threw the first spadeful of earth into the grave. When he heard it strike the coffin, Edmond fainted. His father-in-law and his wife carried him back home, followed by his sisters. Anne, who remained motionless on her knees beside the grave, her eyes brimming with tears, gazing heavenwards, roused everyone's feelings of compassion. The two priests brought her home themselves, long after the ceremony had ended. When she had recovered her senses, as if emerging from a deep trance, her first words were 'Where is my son?' He came to her, still supported by his father-in-law, whilst Marie Dondaine came to Anne's aid, undressed her and put her to bed.

No one ate or drank that day of the wedding and the funeral. Everyone departed as he had come, with grief in his heart, not wanting any refreshment. But Marie remained behind to help her husband and mother-in-law and to comfort her sisters-in-law. For three whole days and nights, she stayed up without rest and without undressing. Touched by her kindness and her zeal, Edmond finally took it upon himself to address her, feeling that he owed it to her, 'You deserved a happier and more joyful lot, my dear wife, but you have generously shared our grief and tears. May God bless you. As for me, I shall be eternally grateful.'

'I would rather weep with you than be happy apart from you. Your grief is justified and shows your natural goodness, Edmond; do not try to restrain it. Allow me to share it with you, as everything we have in common, even tears, is dear to me.'

I obtained all these details from the rough draft of a letter which my father wrote to M. Pombelins, eight days after his wedding. This moving letter, which began straightforwardly, with no preamble, contained a simple account of the events. It ended as follows:

'I have done my duty, dear and worthy father. I shall hide nothing, since it would be unworthy of me as a man and as the son of Pierre R. (whom God has taken to his bosom) if I told you that I was sick at heart. One must accept one's fate as a man. But I can at least express my warmest wishes for the happiness of Mlle Rose and Mlle Eugénie. May those worthy daughters of the best of fathers and the most respected of mothers find as much happiness as I have lost. That is the deepest wish a human heart could make on their behalf. My eyes are blurred with tears. I leave off, oh worthy, worthy father, who will never be mine.

Edme Rétif.

Three months later, Edmond received the following reply.

My dear R.

It was only two days ago that I showed your letter to my
family. I have been deeply affected ever since I heard from
you, and, though I give you my blessing because of your
obedience, I regret the loss of a son-in-law after my own
heart, of whom ill-fortune deprives me. Yes, my dear son, for
that is what you are in friendship and esteem, I commend you.
I have shed tears on your behalf, but they were accompanied
by pleasurable feelings of admiration. Rose, however . . . My
pen and my thoughts stop. I shall not commit the crime of
speaking of a woman's feelings to someone else's husband.
Finally, the day before yesterday, weary and moved by
compassion, I entered my wife's room with your letter in my
hand. She was seated with one of her daughters on her knee.
Eugénie was working silently beside her.

'The poor lad has written', I told them.

'He has written!' said my wife.

'Yes. But I received the letter three months ago. I couldn't
bring myself to show it to you or the children any sooner.
Alas! How he has suffered and how splendidly he's behaved.
You will pity and admire him.'

My words almost caused these three dear womanfolk of
mine to faint. One reached out her arms to me, but I did not
respond. I sat down and began to read your account, my
friend, from your arrival in Auxerre to the moment when you
took up your pen to write to me. There is no point in my
describing to you the effect this had. Only Eugénie blamed
you, and that was out of friendship.

What a good son! What a good lad you are! Why couldn't I
have made you happy! Yet, in spite of everything, my dear
friend, I have to admire your wife's fine qualities. What
engaging candour, what noble sincerity! I keep hearing those
words of hers: 'Everything we have in common is dear to
me, even tears.' One of my daughters picked up this remark
and said how much she cherished her for it. Good and gentle
creature, may she be blessed! She is not responsible for
anything that has happened, my dear Rétif, but she may well
be the source of your happiness.

You can see that I am beginning to adopt your ways and your expressions. That is because your ways are right and your words are spoken from the heart.

It is however necessary, I believe, that our correspondence should be intermittent, my dear boy, both on your side and on ours. Eugénie has a generous nature and is a great consolation to me. I will tell you about it one day perhaps. For the present, I beg you, you who are as dear and as close to me as a son, to go on as you have begun, heeding the advice and counsel of dear lawyer Rétif. M. Molé sends his greetings. This dear friend has not been fortunate with his son-in-law. There is only one Edmond. Farewell, farewell dear fellow, you who are loved and rightfully so, just as others are hated.

I am, with warmest affection and deepest respect, your devoted friend, Antoine Pombelins.

P.S. My wife sends her greetings, in which others share. I did not want to write this, but by hand willed it and my heart commanded it in spite of my better judgement.

Let us take up again the thread of events. Edmond remained with his new wife in his mother's house for eight days. On the third morning, lawyer Rétif arrived. He said not a word as he entered, but looked toward the place where his friend was usually seated and let out a deep sigh.

'The dear man, so awesome yet so beloved, concealed from me that he intended to marry his son so as to prevent . . . The cruel, dear man.'

'Oh cousin', replied Anne Simon, who was alone in the house, 'your arrival here amongst the wretched and the afflicted is like the visit of a guardian angel. Don't be cross with my son; as for dear . . . (a sob replaced his name) you cannot bear him any ill will. He can no longer defend himself or answer you in any way.'

'Oh no, I bear him no ill will. God grant him peace. But recount to me, cousin, the strange things which have reached my ears, the hasty and secret marriage which took place before a father's open grave.'

Anne gave him an exact account of what had happened, or as much as her grief allowed. When she had finished, her worthy relation, beside himself with emotion, cried out:

'I recognise well enough Pierre's hand in it, but your son Edmond has surpassed all my expectation. May he be blessed. He will be a consolation to you in your old age and will bring honour to our name. Where is he, so that I can embrace him?'

Just as he finished speaking, Marie Dondaine entered, busy with the housework. She bowed modestly to the stranger and went up to her mother-in-law to embrace her and wipe away her tears, without saying a word, for she came from a place where the people are very taciturn.

'Who is this kind, obliging person?' asked M. Rétif.

'She's my daughter-in-law.'

'Ah, excuse me ma'am, excuse me cousin.'

'I forgive you, sir, for your obliging remark about me.'

'Where is your husband, my dear'? asked Anne.

'He is doing his duty', (what she meant was that he had gone to weep on his father's grave, as he did three times a day, once he had seen to everything else).

'Is he far away', asked the lawyer.

Marie Dondaine, who did not wish to explain further in front of her mother-in-law, offered to take her kind relation to him. He went with her.

On the way, she explained where her husband was.

'Go back to your mother's side, cousin. I will hasten to find Edmond. I need to see him; I want to see him.'

He found the most loving of sons, prostrate upon the cold stone which covered his father's body. He knelt down without being seen, and when he had finished his prayers he raised his voice and said, weeping:

'Oh Pierre, my childhood friend, the companion of my youth, the dearest of my relations, who could have known a fortnight ago, when I found you so absorbed and so pensive, that it would be the last time I saw my friend and companion of my youth. Alas, alas! How wretched we are! We all die little by little as we lose our friends, and the most wretched is not the one like you who dies in his prime.'

When he heard these tender words of grief, Edmond got up and, throwing his arms around his worthy cousin's neck, interrupted his lament. And as they clasped each other, their tears and sobs were mingled. Then they walked slowly back to the house, and, as they covered the short distance, Edmond told his second father what Anne did not know. He spoke of M. Molé, of Mlle Pombelins, of his own feelings and of the sacrifice he had made.

We respond warmly in our family to whatever seems fine and noble, and our response sometimes overwhelms us, as it did on this occasion. Our worthy cousin Jean R. (may God bless him as he has done in his children) halted in silent admiration.

'Pity you', he remarked warmly, no, no, no! I envy you. You are truly fortunate. I am jealous of you and of your father, even though he is dead. It is envy rather than pity that I feel. I knew we had passion and spirit and a sense of humour, worthy of our stock, but our moral strength is nowhere greater than in you, and you are only twenty. Never let it degenerate, Edmond. Whether you are rich or poor does not matter. Your lot is chosen, your fortune beyond compare. Oh my forefathers! If you look down on your worthy heir from your heavenly abode, what joy must fill your purified souls! And you Rose, what a prize you have lost!

I have met your wife, my friend. She told me where you were. May heaven bless the worthy woman, for, if I am not mistaken, she will be another Anne Simon.'

The warmth with which he spoke momentarily eased Edmond's grief and raised his spirits. For the third time he was glad he had made a noble sacrifice.

It is not my intention to give a complete account of all my father's actions, as many are simply part of his everyday life. I will just record that he went to live in Saci and served his father-in-law for seven years, during which time he had seven children by Marie Dondaine; that he suffered a great deal on account of his father-in-law Thomas's ill-humour, but put up with it patiently for his wife's sake, who was a truly excellent woman; that his period of servitude (for this is indeed what it was, since Edmond's desire to help his mother and three sisters meant that he wore himself out with work) ended with the death of the respected Marie; and that he remained a widower for seven years. But there are some details I must record.

I will say only a word or two about some of Edme R's.

children, especially his daughters, of whom there were five.
But I might perhaps be allowed to dwell a little on his sons at
the proper time and place. The eldest, above all, who is one of
the most respected of the lower order of priests within the
church, might be thought of as the recompense for Edmond's
virtues and for his obedience to his father's wishes in the choice
of a wife. Although he is still alive, I shall not shrink from
praising such a worthy minister, certain as I am that this work
will not reach him in his remote sanctuary nor threaten his
modesty and humility.

Of the five daughters he had by his first wife, several were
shapely and quite good-looking. Especially the second, who is
the image of her elder brother, as he is of his father. The second
son by the first marriage, who was called Thomas after his
maternal grandfather, looks like his mother and has her goodness together with Edme R's open-heartedness. I cannot mention the eldest without referring to his younger brother. They
live together, and you will see from the account I shall give
what an example they afford of the sublime and gentle teaching
of the gospel.

Once Edmond was widowed, prudence and a concern for
the well-being of his young family meant that he could no
longer remain in his father-in-law's house. He took his leave of
him and began to work on his own, which he had not done
before. (It had gone against his conscience to work for Thomas
Dondaine, who was a rich man and should have provided for
his own children as a father). But a sense of obligation to his
wife had dictated his behaviour, a rare example indeed of a man
prepared to sacrifice his own interest to the peace of mind and
happiness of a woman he had married out of obedience.

Before describing all the things my father did, thus enabling
the reader to appreciate them, I must give him some idea of the
state of the parish of Saci when he went to live there.

Formerly, people talked of 'the scroungers of Saci', because
almost all the inhabitants used to beg, which was not surprising, since they had such poor land. The land around Nitri, on
the other hand, was good, and the inhabitants lived comfortably. The situation has certainly changed today, as it is the
people of Nitri, in spite of their good land, who beg from those
of Saci.

One can say the same thing about the prosperity of a village as one can about the victories of an army: one simply needs a good leader as men are everywhere the same. Edmond R. brought to Saci his skill in utilizing them properly, and it has remained with them. When he was living with his father-in-law and merely carrying out his orders, he began to suggest ways of improving the land in a district of the parish which was not particularly promising. Even its name suggests its nature; 'saxiacus' in Latin, from 'saxo' (stone). The land is in fact covered with huge lumps of stone, which might be of some use, were they within easy reach of a large town. But the village is isolated and the stone so easily quarried, that each year the soil becomes more arid as another layer is unearthed.

Edmond's first experiment was made in a field belonging to his father-in-law. Beneath the stones, he discovered dark, rich soil, and so he sacrificed the top part of the field, which was completely unploughable, and piled the stones up there. Although it is the hardest job on the land, he applied himself indefatigably and got the servants to help him. He took care forming the base of the cairn (which is what these piles are called) with the largest stones, and built it up until it were as tall as a man, filling in the gaps with clumps of rye-grass and other such grasses. They bound it together at the bottom and provided almost as much grazing for the cattle as the land on which it was built. He also remembered to make a kind of spiral staircase up to the top, so that each year, before ploughing started, stones which had been unco-vered by the rain could be placed on top.

There is no better way of improving soil than removing stones. The crop from that field was double what it had been in an ordinary year and repaid the labour spent on it that one year alone. Each year thereafter, it yielded a clear profit. I have often heard my father express the wish that prisoners be used as stone-gatherers before their trial. They could be placed in the charge of soldiers who would be brought from their barracks, where they are garrisoned with nothing to occupy them. In certain cases, he suggested that it might even be appropriate to sentence men to this kind of labour rather than to the galleys. Their work could be properly supervised by one of the officials of the parish concerned. He also thought that such people should be employed in the rechannelling of rivers which cut into good grazing land, leaving only a sandy bank on the other side.

In spite of his success, Edme R. met with opposition from his father-in-law and was prevented from building a second cairn. A few of the villagers followed his example, but as they had not taken care to make the base firm and fill in the gaps with sods, the stones were soon spread all over their land. Edme R's. cairn, on the other hand, is still standing after sixty years and serves as a monument to him.

As soon as Edme was his own master, he used the talents which nature had bestowed on him in the first and noblest of arts. He showed considerable skill with the plough and took account of the nature of the land, letting the share cut deeply, or lightly skimming the surface depending on the depth of the top soil. If it was thin, he took care not to bring up the arid sub-soil and not to uncover stones. Indeed, he was so skilled that one could pick out the land he had ploughed because his stalks were six inches taller than those of his neighbours. When the inhabitants of Saci saw how successful he was, they immediately followed his example. The barren hillcrests were covered with cairns and the surrounding fields began to produce crops.

Soon the farmers were encouraged to clear the uncultivated land of the parish, which was at least a third of the total. Edmond R. again set the example. Ploughing land like this is arduous and might well be costly in terms of man-power, not to mention the fact that, on this poor soil, there were few hands to spare. In order not to waste a single strip of plough-land, Edme set to work on the abandoned and uncultivated fields which he wanted to reclaim. After this first ploughing, he sowed oats. The crop grew quite well, though the weeds grew even thicker. But Edmond didn't mind as he was adequately rewarded for the few days he had spent ploughing with an excellent crop of fodder, which this newly cultivated land produced. The land had been broken up a little, and after it had been re-ploughed three times, it was ready to be sown with wheat the following year. If the land was covered with thorns and juniper bushes, they had to be grubbed out. Yet even this extra labour was not in vain, as the bushes provided kindling for the bread oven.

Yet this represented only half the work that needed to be done in the parish. Edme R. noticed that it was impossible to cultivate several hillsides because they sloped too steeply. In those days, the inhabitants produced so little wine that the former lords of the manor, charging them the exhorbitant tithe on such bad land of one sheaf in twelve, as well as one sheaf per acre, had neglected to levy anything on their vines. At his own expense, Edmond made a trial planting on part of one of those unploughable slopes. Seven years effort and outlay are scarcely enough to create a vineyard, but it finally produced an excellent wine, which was spoilt by a certain lack of body; that is to say, it was drinkable in six months but did not retain its goodness beyond three years.

The hard-working men of Saci imitated him by planting vines on the uncultivated slopes, and because they were created from nothing, the return was soon greater than that on their own land. But this wasn't achieved all at once. It took nearly thirty years' cultivation to reach the level of perfection and the yields which they have today.

It was soon realised that the life of a vineyard was barely twenty years on this arid soil, and that the vines had to be renewed quite frequently. Edmond was the first to become aware of this problem and to seek a remedy. Once they had reduced the area of fallow land, they increased the number of working animals, and, as they became richer, they acquired other stock, cows, sheep and goats, which made life easier and more comfortable. They then had to grow more fodder, but this in turn was beneficial for their agriculture, as they produced more manure. There was a very good meadow in the valley where the village was situated, but at that time only half of it produced a reasonable crop. Edmond thought of creating artificial meadows where the vines were rooted out, which could be used for seven or eight years and would thus rest the soil sufficiently before vines were replanted. He knew what to plant from the nature of the soil, having noticed lucerne growing on the hilltops in the places where the rains hadn't washed the earth away. So he sowed this mountain plant when he cleared his vines, and he had the satisfaction of growing excellent fodder without losing a single year's yield from this land. The practice was immediately adopted in the neighbourhood, and today whenever someone gives up an old vineyard, it is said that lucerne is planted. Since the yield from this crop is light in the first year, the old vine stocks are left in the ground for the few grapes which they give. The following winter, they are cut off at the base and the young shoots are cut with the following season's growth of lucerne, thus increasing its bulk. The vines finally die when they are cut with a scythe.

Although Edmond spent at least thirty years on these various projects, I have dealt with them together, as they are linked, and I don't wish to return to them. I have already mentioned that only part of the best meadow in Saci produced a good crop. Even this part was often flooded, and no one had done anything to prevent it. Edmond advised them to dig a deep, wide ditch in the middle of the field, so that the water could drain into it. Once this was done, the yield was doubled and of much higher quality. There was, however, much work to be done on the other part, which was rather poor and only served as rough grazing land. Edmond owned quite a large piece of it, and, some distance away, bordering on the meadow, he had a field covered with a pile of huge stones, which had rolled down from the hillside when this was cultivated. Edmond dug a wide ditch, ten feet deep, in the middle of his meadow and had all the stones brought from his other field, and piled them up eight feet high in the ditch. He then put a layer of clay a foot thick over the bed of stones and four feet of soil on top of that. Finally, he replaced the turves, which had been carefully preserved. The ground was now three and a half feet above its original level. Alongside, another ditch was dug and filled in the same way and so on until the whole plot had been covered. What was the result of all this? The floods came, but Edme R's. field was like an island of green above the water level and produced a fine, clean, thick hay. He was certainly rewarded for his outlay on this field, as it also produced the best wheat they had ever grown in the district.

The following autumn, all his neighbours did as he had done. Some even fetched stones from their most distant fields.

Today, this area of meadow gives the best crops. All this goes
to show how profitable one man's example can be in a parish,
when, instead of directing his energies to greedy ends and
taking over other people's land, he makes good use of them,
and far from harming others brings them benefits. As a result,
the prosperity which Edme R. enjoyed never gave rise to
envy.

Having heard favourable reports of my father's activities,
worthy lawyer Rétif visited him in the midst of his labours.
He was full of admiration, and, as my father was out in the
fields when he arrived, he went to the respected priest,
Antoine Foudriat, to find out what was happening before
going to see his cousin. He couldn't keep back his tears when
he saw my father come in, covered in sweat, and, as he threw
his arms around his neck, he said to him:

'Dear Edmond, when I look at you I see the hand of God
inspiring a father's commands to his son. Who would not
have judged our respected Pierre's behaviour an act of folly,
had he known of the prospects and the happiness which you
were obliged to renounce? And yet, how fortunate they are in
this community that your father was inspired by God to
summon you home, in order to exercise those precious talents
on which the well-being of the whole parish depends. What
does it matter that you have suffered? Is there an honest man
who would not envy your lot? Oh worthy cousin Edmond, I
envy you myself, and for my sons. You are a credit to our
name. I know the reputation you have already earned. Your
grandfather, my respected uncle, was called 'the just man'. He
lives again in you. And the expression everyone uses
whenever they mention your name is 'the just man'. What a
splendid title, given so willingly and so freely by everyone in
the district, my dear friend and cousin, to someone who is not
yet thirty-six. God bless you, Edmond, and your father for
bringing you back among us, and may God grant him his
reward. God bless your mother who nursed you and who
brought you up to respect hard work and to do your duty,
and who set you a loving, precious example.'

This warm expression of emotion from the heart of an
upright man is offered here as the climax of my account of my
father's labours on the land. But the most satisfying reward

for him, and the one most worthy of him, was to leave behind
at his death a thriving parish, whose inhabitants had in the
main begged for their bread when he came and who were now
the most comfortably off in the district. The fate of Nitri was
the exact opposite. I have explained the reason for this in the
first volume of *L'Ecole des Pères*, to which I refer my readers.

Edme's concern for the good and for the happiness of the
parish in which he settled, out of obedience to his father, did
not end there. He did many good deeds before he had
occasion, in his capacity as judge, to exercise that great
generosity of spirit which was at the heart of his character.

In conversations which he had with the old men of the
community, he often heard them regret the loss of common
woodland which had been taken over by a neighbouring lord in
whose domain it was situated. But these poor peasants made
only vague complaints and their wishes had no influence.

'Are there deeds?' Edme R. asked them.

'There were, but we don't know what has become of
them.'

He gathered information, questioned the old men, and one
day old Daugi, who was the oldest of them, told him, 'If our
deeds have not been burnt, they must be in the hands of the
son of our former bailiff who was here sixty years ago. He is
now a very old man and the priest of Annet-la-Côte.'

Once he made his discovery, Edme R. lost no time in setting
out on horseback for Annet. He arrived there in the evening
and found the old priest. But he was almost in his dotage and
could give him no information. All that Edme could now do
was to talk to his housekeeper, but she knew nothing about
the matter. They gave him supper and put him up for the
night, as it was dark when he arrived.

The next day the kind housekeeper said to him, 'Sir, I was
thinking about what you said to me in the night, and I
remembered that the priest has some old documents on the
canopy over his bed. If you wish to see them, wait until he has
got up as they are covered with so much dust that it would
blind him.'

Edme R. gave a start when he heard this and was most
impatient for the priest to get up. At last he was allowed to go
and look through the documents, which had been lying there

for more than forty years, untouched by anyone. He found them all, except for one, not the least important, which had unfortunately been used to cover a pot of grape jelly sent to Paris. Once he had removed all the dust, which prevented him from deciphering anything, my father discovered the crucial deed, according to which the common woodland had been granted by a former lord to the inhabitants of Saci in recognition of good and faithful service which they had given. He was so full of excitement that he did not bother to examine the others, having been assured that there was nothing in them relating to the priest's personal affairs.

He set out straight away even though a storm was brewing, and he got caught in it. His sole concern, however, was to keep the deeds dry, which he only just managed to do. But his eagerness to return home cost him dear and he nearly died of pleurisy, which simply goes to show that one's best actions bring no material reward. Even in the state in which he was on his return, he hurried to see the priest to tell him of his discovery. The good man was delighted, but showed too much interest in the news and too little concern at that moment for the bearer. The two men resolved to leave no stone unturned in order that their parishioners should regain their rights.

My father's illness delayed the execution of their plan for several weeks, but as soon as he recovered they set to work. The priest pursued the proceedings in Dijon, whilst Edme R. worked to effect a conciliation with the neighbouring lord, who was the unlawful possessor of the common woodland. He achieved it finally, and the parties made an agreement, whereby the inhabitants regained possession without reclaiming any of their former rights. The lord who granted them this possession was given a seat of honour in the church. Edme R. did all that was humanly possible to prevent him from becoming an enemy of the community. Once this task was completed, Edme R. was the most respected citizen in the parish.

My father excelled in all aspects of husbandry and above all in the care of cattle. He left the smaller livestock to the women and servants, and was content simply to look them over once a day. He alone was responsible for the horses. I have already

spoken of his love for this noble animal, but his feelings were
secondary to his awareness of its usefulness and of his own
prosperity, and they were governed by reason. Because of his
particular way with horses, his knowledge of them was
considerable, and he would have been an excellent horse-
dealer had he taken up his trade. But he had too high a regard
for agriculture to abandon it. All the horses he bought
changed visibly in his hands. When he got them, they were
usually young and thin and he would work them for two
years before selling them for what they were worth. He was
so fair and so knowledgeable, that everyone let him fix the
price. On a number of occasions he was known to have
lowered the price which the buyer first offered when he
inspected the animal. It was his absolute integrity together
with his other virtues, about which I shall speak shortly,
which earned him the title of 'the honest man', by which he
was known throughout the district and which still echoes in
his children's ears whenever they return home.

I have already given one illustration of the way in which a
horse showed its affection at having a good master, and I
could give you many more.

One day, when he was ploughing, a company of recruits,
which was crossing the kingdom to reach its destination,
came to ask him for horses to ride three leagues. Edme R.
agreed but told them that they could only be handled by him
as they were so wild and unbroken. The braggarts laughed at
him and mounted, two on each horse. As long as Edme was
holding their bridles these frisky animals obeyed him, and
they remained obedient as long as they could hear his commands. But when they were some distance away, one of them
turned, despite the efforts of the two soldiers, and seeing his
master returning home reared up twice, throwing his riders to
the ground, and raced after him neighing. The three other
horses, hearing the neighing and seeing their companion
disappear, did exactly the same and galloped after their
master. Anyone other than Edme R. would have enjoyed this
incident. He had in fact sent a servant with the horses, and he
now went after them himself. He made the soldiers remount,
held the friskiest by the halter and then walked the three
leagues, though it was an extremely hot day. All he asked of

the soldiers was that they treat his horses gently, which they were obliged to do in their own interest.

When he reached Noyers, M. Miré, the mayor of the town and a relative of his, was scandalised to see him arrive like this and wanted to have the soldiers put in prison. But Edme R. intervened on their behalf and accepted their apologies.

'We took you for a simple peasant', the officer told him.

'You are not mistaken, sir; but what you don't realise is that I am proud of it.'

My other illustration is more exemplary, since the horse involved saved my father's life. Coming back on one occasion from Tonnerre, he was attacked by four robbers as he entered a wood near Chichée. One took his horse's bridle, another held a pistol, whilst the two others ordered him to dismount and went through his pockets and his saddlebags. My father was frightened at first and didn't say a word, but then a thought came to him which made him bolder. 'These men will just as likely kill me whether I hand over my purse or refuse to give it to them, if their safety depends on it. I'll try to escape and see what happens', he said to himself in a flash. So he gave his horse a command which he only used when it faced some huge obstacle, 'Come on, boy'. At the same time he kicked it, which was most unusual for him as he never used spurs. At this, the animal set off, even though the robber was still holding the bridle, and dragged him twenty paces at full gallop with his master still urging him on. Finally, he shook the man off and trampled him under foot. Had it not been for his affection for his master and his readiness to obey his command, Edme R. would have been killed.

The other animals were equally fond of him. He was fair and kind to his fellow-men and showed the same fairness and kindness to all creatures of a lower order. When he went up to them, he always had something in his hand, even the stupidest were attracted to him.

They had on the farm a young bull, a huge well-fed beast that never worked. (Edme R. kept him to serve the cows in the village and so produce better stock, as the common cowherds only bought the weakest bullocks.) This particular animal was so fierce that no one could get near him and he had to be left loose in the yard. Yet as soon as his master appeared, the bull would bound up to him, follow him into the garden without straying, and eat grass out of his hand. Edme would then lead him to his pen and tether him, and the only resistance he offered was a few plaintive bellows. It's a valuable asset for a countryman to be loved and feared by his animals, and those who have it get much more out of these humble working animals than those who rely on force.

It is almost impossible to describe the affection which the dogs showed towards my father, and on numerous occasions people enjoyed putting them to the test in amazing ways. I cannot relate them all but I will tell you one touching story.

My father lived on a farm called La Bretonne, which is totally isolated and only joined to the village by quite a large walled enclosure. He often complained that the gates were not closed properly, so that it was easy to open them from the outside. One day, when he was coming back from the fields, he decided to try to get in without knocking. With a little difficulty he managed to dislodge the bar which was placed across the inside of the door and succeeded in getting in. Amongst the dogs which he had at that time was a red, half-greyhound bitch, a first-class guard dog, keeping wolves away from the flocks as well as being good at catching hares. Because of these skills, she was especially useful on the farm and a particular favourite of her master, to whom she was exceptionally attached. He would sometimes say laughingly, 'After my family I have never had better companions than Touslesjours, Germain (an excellent ploughboy), Flamand (one of the horses I have mentioned) and Friquette (which was the name of the dog)'. When she heard the slight noise he made trying to get the door open, Friquette of course crept towards it but did not bark, as she usually did, because she was preparing to do something much worse to what she thought was a thief. When the bar dropped, my father squeezed one leg and then half his body through to open it. But immediately he felt the dog seize his leg. Friquette didn't bite him however, as she smelt her master, but let out a terrible yowl that frightened everyone in the house. They rushed into the courtyard with a light and saw their master, with the dog rolling on the ground in front of him, letting out dreadful, piercing whines. As he advanced, she crept up to his feet wanting to be stroked. He didn't pay much attention to her as he was more concerned to make them realise the possible consequences of not closing the door. But when he got indoors, the dog continued to cringe, jumped onto the chairs, howling, and then rolled over at his feet again as if out of breath. He scolded her to make her be quiet, but she let out the most indescribable noises and great tears fell from her eyes. Her master had to talk gently to her and pat her as he gave her her food. At this point they managed to put her out quite easily, which until then had been impossible even though they had lost patience and hit her a few times with a whip. For eight whole days, without making a sound, she tried to show her master that she was sorry in such a genuine and touching way that everyone was moved. In order to cure her of this, he had to take her with him whenever he went out and to show by the way he treated her that he had forgiven her. Oh Descartes! you should have studied nature more closely before inventing your ingenious systems.

I have told how my father sold his horses after working them for two years (this made sound economic sense, though there were exceptions). Indeed, by adopting this practice, all the horses which he bought during his long life cost him nothing, once he had made the initial outlay. It was in fact a lucrative business; the only one in which he engaged. But here I shall simply describe the way he bought and sold them.

Having already said something about my father's method of selling, I would just like to add that he never bothered about the buyer's solvency, not because he lacked judgement, but out of human kindness. As a result, he never grew rich, which he might well have done by using his natural talents and without abandoning his scrupulous fairness. But when a poor man came to him in tears, saying that his horse had died of old age, he couldn't refuse him another, and was happy to accept his gratitude instead of money. He never once used a bailiff to collect his debts and he accepted the smallest payments on account. Often, when he went on his rounds, instead of collecting his debts, he lent his debtors money to help them pay their tithes. Conduct such as this earned him the heartfelt thanks of women and children when he arrived in their village. Hard-working and thrifty, he never felt that he had wasted time and efforts, if he had helped a neighbour. At his death, we found unredeemed bonds to the value of two thousand crowns which he had allowed to lapse, together with the following comment: 'These people are poor and of good will'. Small payments had been made on some of them. I will not disguise the fact that my mother sometimes remonstrated with him over what she termed his negligence about being paid. His reply on these occasions was:

'Wife, we have bread, wine and a little more besides. These folk are our bretheren and they do not have the necessities of life. God forbid that I should cause them to starve to death by taking their last mouthful. You yourself would not wish that.'

'What about our own children?'

'I want them to have a good inheritance, and with your help, wife, and the splendid example you set, they will have an income of one thousand crowns.' Seeing her astonishment, he went on 'Your example and mine will teach them to make do with just a little in life. No tobacco, no wine, no gambling; that is worth five hundred francs a year. Being hard on themselves, not putting any trust in doctors and their remedies, having a taste for hard work and a good understanding of money affairs; that is worth more than fifteen hundred livres, two thousand francs a year. Having no time for coquetry, recognising the value of useful work, of whatever kind, and showing complete disdain and contempt for idleness, whatever fancy name one gives it; that is worth one thousand francs. That's already a thousand crowns. Earning the good will of all those with whom one does business is worth a great deal. Teaching them to value the middle station of life, as we both do, and inspiring them with a love of honesty, justice, unselfishness, liberty even; instilling in them the firm belief that riches are nothing; that a contented heart and a quiet conscience are a hundred times preferable, and that at the hour of death the most powerful king on earth and the most wretched drover, who is out in all winds and weathers, are made equal again for all eternity; these things, wife, are priceless. Believe me, we shall leave our children a greater and more glorious heritage than any duke or peer of the realm.'

Whenever he bought a piece of land, he would determine whether the seller should keep it and would exhort him not to

part with his inheritance. If it was absolutely necessary and
decided upon, he would buy it at a fair price, and, since he was
aware that land was gradually increasing in value, he would add
on to the price whatever the inheritance would have been
worth in ten years time. If the seller was a poor man, he
would give him two or three bushels of grain as a present for
his own use and for his livestock, a few days after the sale.
And so, anything which came up for sale was offered to him
before anyone else. In those cases where a relative exercised
his right to buy back what had been sold, he never contested
it. He did not even demand payment in cash, willingly
accepting a bond, on which no interest was payable.

It only remains for me to say something of the way he
administered justice.

He became a notary early on, from the time of his first
marriage, and he acted in this capacity throughout his life. But
it brought him very little and his heirs barely received the
small sums he had advanced for registering deeds.

He was appointed judge by the Knight Commander of
Malta, who was lord of the village, at the death of maître
Boujat who had held the post for forty years. My father did not
seek to obtain this position but was granted it after a secret
deputation of twelve inhabitants sought it on his behalf. He
accepted with gratitude the conferment of this appointment,
but apologised for his lack of competence.

'If you are unable to do the job, the commander wrote to
him, I shall not accept your resignation, knowing your good
will, but I shall give you an assistant. Thus you need have no
qualms. Moreover, the judgements you gave as a former
servant of the law during your predecessor's illness do not
suggest incompetence but excellent judgement, which pleased
me greatly. You can only grow in experience and wisdom.
Thus I hope that you will win approval for my nomination
which was ardently sought by my vassals.'

The Commander of Saulce-lès-Auxerre.

If Edmond's nomination was sought by the local people and
if he performed his duties to their satisfaction, the same cannot
be said of other practitioners. As there were very few educated
people in the village, the deputy officers of the law and even
the procurator fiscal were from Vermanton, a large town one

league from Saci. It did not take them long to realise that
instead of giving them work, the new judge was taking work
from them by avoiding legal proceedings and achieving as
many settlements as possible. That is how he spent Sunday
afternoons and feast-days, except when there were services.
They complained bitterly to him, but he felt that there was no
need to pay any heed to such complaints.

Luckily Edme R. was supported by the procurator fiscal,
whose position often makes its occupant the scourge of the
peasant community. This official, who was called maître
Boudard, lived in Vermanton like the others, but he was the
son of one of Marie Dondaine's sisters. Besides being an honest
man, whose financial standing raised him above the position he
occupied, he showed his uncle all the respect he deserved. He
consulted him on all the charges he brought and followed his
advice in trying to prevent disorder rather than punish it,
without however giving any encouragement to vice through
undue negligence.

From another quarter, Master Antoine Foudriat, a priest of
rare ability, gave these two men his support whenever it
furthered his sacred ministry. As he was an extremely clever
and well-educated man with a gift above all for guiding
people, he lent weight to the regulations they drew up by
taking the trouble to point out their usefulness from the
pulpit. Such wise and valuable agreement between the representatives of authority who govern men's behaviour is the
surest means of bringing happiness, as long as the priest and
the magistrate have sound and moderate views. Thus,
Antoine Foudriat one day told his parishioners: 'You have
two ministers, my children, God's minister, which I am
honoured to be, and another who represents the law. Both are
equally worthy of respect in their ministry and both are God's
representatives, as far as you are concerned. The judge and
myself are like fathers, and we are both concerned only for
your well-being, as it has been our good fortune, I believe, to
make clear to you.' He made these remarks after the law-court
had decreed that the people of Saci could take possession of
their woodland, and they aroused such feelings of emotion
that the priest and the newly appointed judge were carried in
triumph from the church.

However, the occasion on which the Saci judge showed his propensity for doing good, and displeased still further the court officials, was in drawing up inventories when people died. He was so moved by the plight of poor orphans and the bereaved widow that he dealt with everything in one sitting, and even went without his fees.

'You certainly do things in a hurry!' they remarked.

'Yes, you are right', he replied with a laugh. 'And, believe me, I am as interested in getting on with the job as you are in delaying it. As you have sometimes been heard to remark yourselves, one's actions are the true measure of one's own interest.'

Edme's reputation for wisdom and integrity soon spread throughout the district. People who had affairs to settle came from neighbouring villages (I have seen it myself), either to consult him or to accept his arbitration. He was ready to hear people's cases every feast-day, as if he were a magistrate in a large town. He discussed most willingly the affairs of these good people, but only after he had dealt with those of his own villagers, and he would apologise to them, saying: 'My friends, one has to settle one's debts before one can perform acts of charity.' Sometimes these strangers would bring presents of game or poultry. He would not humiliate them by suggesting they take them back, but he would insist that they received something in return to the same value, whether in the form of money or provisions for their own use. When it became known that this was what he did, strangers (those of his own community would not have dared take the liberty) would furtively enter the courtyard and let cockerels and pullets loose without anyone noticing. As a result, no one knew anything about it until the evening when these poor young birds tried to find somewhere to roost. They were the only presents he kept, as he did not know who to blame.

He never took any money from strangers for the advice he gave them, even when it involved making a journey to see something for himself. And as he always visited them on feast-days, he used to say that, according to the scriptures, one should not receive any reward for one's labours.

Certain parishioners, who were more zealous than enlightened, were scandalised by his absence on feast-days. But when

Antoine Foudriat got to hear of this, he told his parishioners from the pulpit that their judge was never absent on account of his own personal business, and that christian charity was the best way of keeping Sundays and feast-days holy. Vindication from such a respected priest as Antoine Foudriat put an end to the murmuring, and prevented any outcry.

As well as all the good works which he performed for his community (which were so considerable that it is flourishing today whereas it was in penury when he arrived), there are others which I have not yet mentioned. Over a period of thirty years he made a series of observations on the recurring pattern of good and bad years, which was especially helpful to vinegrowers, the fruit of whose labours is often lost through frost. These observations consisted principally of an annual forecast of the weather in general, for example if the winter would be long, cold or rainy, the summer hot and dry or cold and damp, if there would be late spring frosts etc. These calendars often proved useful to him. One year especially (it was 1749), he was convinced that there would be late frosts and so he delayed the pruning of his vines. There was a frost in the middle of May and only the tips of the shoots were touched, although the growth of the vine was checked as a result. On another occasion (in 1753), he made use of his calendar and brought benefit to the whole community by buying barrels, which were extremely cheap during Lent. He acquired a considerable stock of them and let his neighbours have them on credit. Because it was a good year, barrels which had sold for forty sous in March were selling at four francs one hundred sous in September. I have since read with some admiration that my father, who knew nothing of the Romans and had never heard of Cato, Varro and Columella, followed their example with his calendars. The ancients used to draw up calendars of the patterns of the seasons and give them to each other. They were family heirlooms which were handed down. I noticed one peculiar thing in the ones my father had made. In 1731, I believe it was, it didn't rain from February until September in our area, and this meant there was no hay and no grain for the animals.

I cannot help wondering what Edme R. might have become, had he been born in Rome at the time of Valerius

Publicola and Brutus. To me he is as great as their great men. He lacked only their status, not their virtue.

I shall end the first part of this work with a few remarks which relate to what I said on page forty-six. It is traditionally accepted in our family that our former name was Monroyal or Montroyal and that the surname of Restif or Rétif was joined to it in 1309, at the time of the Knight Templar Jean de Montroyal who, when the order was destroyed, defended it vigorously and truthfully before Philippe le Bel's and Clément V's commissaries. It is believed that this was the origin of the surname 'restif'*, which was also taken by his relatives. These champions of their order were not executed like those heretics who, having confessed out of weakness to crimes which were imputed to them, subsequently retracted (see Dupuis).

The late M. Rétif, who was priest of Auxonne and one of lawyer Rétif's sons, knew a great deal about our family history, on which he had done private research. But because he lacked authentic documents, he published nothing. His father often used to say, 'Our new name is respected, but we know little of our former name.' It is from the priest of Auxonne that we learned that in 1582 Charles Restif, a protestant who lived in the Saint-Amatre district of Auxerre, addressed a petition to King Charles IX on behalf of his fellow calvinists, asking for schools which they would run at their own expense, and offering to give up to catholics those which had been founded. All our titles were lost during the wars of religion, because our ancestors had been amongst the first to embrace the reformed religion and were thus exposed to the worst suffering. I have heard tell that we had relatives in England who kept our former name and called those who remained in France 'restifs'. We were extremely well-connected. However that may be, the only titles which my brothers and I have to be proud of are those my father earned.

* The usual spelling in modern French is 'rétif' and it means stubborn or restive.

BOOK 3

I shall take up the thread of Edme R.'s life at the point at which he was widowed and left his father-in-law's house.

Edme was deeply affected by the death of his virtuous wife. He lost an affectionate and quiet companion, who had always behaved as if she knew nothing of her husband's feelings for another woman, even though she was aware of them. It is also true that for his part he acted reasonably, as if those feelings had never existed.

Burdened as he was with seven children, the eldest of whom was still a child, he needed all the patience and all the good sense he had. He called upon his dear mother for help, and she came and looked after her grandchildren for four years like a mother.

His eldest son was already beginning to show signs of what he would become one day. But the precious child was sickly, and at twelve he had to undergo a most serious operation. He bore it with such piety and long-suffering that it is still remembered to this day. When he had recovered and might have been of some help, his grandfather took charge of him on the pretext that he would see to his education. He began his studies, but my father would not allow someone else to pay for his lodgings. In the natural order of things the liability was his, and he had no intention of falling behind with the payments.

In 1725, the third year of his widowhood, Edme R. had to go to the capital on business, and he took with him some samples of his own first wine and that of the other villagers. He lodged at an inn, but his first visit was to maître Molé, of whom he had heard nothing for ten years. The honest old man was in great adversity, having been ruined by financial speculation. Edme felt deeply for him, and his visit brought his old friend some consolation, as he shared his misfortunes and offered him hospitality of either his own house or that of lawyer Rétif as he pleased.

'What has become of our respected friend?' Edme asked.

With a sigh, M. Molé replied: 'M. Pombelins and his wife
are no more. Rose has married her cousin de Varipon at
Eugénie's request. She was in love with the young man
herself, but she renounced him in favour of her sister,
reasoning thus: "He would make me happy, and there is all
the more reason to suppose that he will bring you happiness,
since you are worthier than I." Eugénie was most concerned
at her sister's grief, for Rose suffered cruelly, Edmond,
though she bore you no ill will once her father had explained
everything. We all admired your behaviour. But I was saying
that Eugénie renounced the man she loved in her sister's
favour. She begged her most earnestly, shed tears, insisted
that she accept him. Rose finally yielded because she admired
her sister's gesture and was moved by other feelings
towards her. It was out of respect, inspired by such rare and
generous motives, that she yielded to her, she said. M. de
Varipon is an admirable husband and Rose is an excellent
wife, but neither of them feels any love for the other. They
have the most delightful children one could find. I hope that
you will pay them a visit. As for Eugénie, at her father's
request she married a young man from the provinces, who,
like you, comes from a good family. He is a fine lad. My dear
friend and his wife died, having seen their children as happily
settled as they could have hoped for in the circumstances. As
for me, I have lived to witness my daughter's unhappiness.
We learned from her she was responsible for your father's
strange decision, as a result of the letter she wrote against
herself, fearing he would consent to your marriage were he
asked. She had little faith in your promise, never having met a
young man like you before. Neither had we, I might add,
even though we were older and had more experience of the
world. She alone was responsible for what happened, but
everyone has forgiven her. She lives close to Eugénie. Fortun-
ately, she has no children, so the dishonour which her
husband has brought upon himself and which has made him
rich will at least die with him.

We have refused all the offers of help which he has made,
and his wife receives only the interest from her dowry, which
she shares with us. That is how things stand, Edmond, after

your long absence. We have talked of you almost every day, and I am sure that it would give Mme de Varipon and Mme Bourgeois great pleasure were you to visit them, but I beg you to visit Mme Bourgeois first.'

As he listened to this account, Edmond shed tears in memory of M. Pombelins and his wife. He had expected to find them full of life and had been counting on the worthy man's help and encouragement. He had learnt indirectly of the marriages of the two young ladies without any explanation. He now asked maître Molé if he would take him to Mme Bourgeois.

They called on her together the same day at four in the afternoon. Eugénie was alone when they arrived, surrounded by three lovely children. M. Molé spoke first, and realising that Edmond had not been recognised made a sign to him not to reveal his identity. Then M. Molé's daughter came in and she did not remember him either. Edmond's appearance could scarcely have changed more completely. Twelve years earlier he had been young and fresh looking, but his hands and face were burned by the sun and in place of his fine head of hair he now wore a rather dishevelled wig. His country clothes were exactly like those of the Burgundian peasants who sold their wine at the gate St-Bernard. He had not spoken yet, for his soft voice would undoubtedly have been recognised.

'I wished to inquire after your health and that of your dear sister as I was passing', said M. Molé.

'Wait one moment', replied Eugénie. 'She will be here shortly with her children. Mme — (M. Molé's daughter) has just gone to fetch her as we have something to arrange together this afternoon.'

Seeing the countryman standing, hat in hand, she remarked, 'M. Molé, you keep Monsieur standing.'

'I am quite alright, Madame,' Edme R. replied, his voice full of emotion.

Eugénie seemed to be trying to recall something, and then, looking at her sister's former suitor, asked M. Molé, 'Am I mistaken? Is it him?'

'Yes, Madame, it really is our Edmond.'

Before he could finish his sentence, Eugénie threw herself eagerly into the countryman's arms and offered him each cheek twice.

'We have such fond hearts that we never forget our friends, even when they forget us,' she remarked. 'You wicked fellow! But if everything we have been told is true, you are not wicked, you are an excellent fellow.'

Edme was so overcome with emotion that he could not reply and the tears rolled down his cheeks. As he listened to Eugénie it was as if the twelve years had not elapsed and he was reliving once again the moment when he left Rose, knowing that he would lose her for ever. It was a painful experience and he shuddered whenever he recalled it.

'I understand his language', said Eugénie, and turning to M. Molé she asked, 'Is he happy? Is he rich or poor?'

'He is even more fortunate. He is a credit to his community and its benefactor.'

At this Eugénie began to weep with emotion. 'We were not mistaken then? Rose will be delighted to learn of it.' Turning to Edmond she asked, 'Have you any children? – Seven, Madame. – Do they have a happy disposition? Are they like you? – By God's grace they are blessed with a happy disposition, and my eldest son is . . . but it is not right that I should sing his praises; ah, Madame, such blessings come from heaven. – He takes after a good father. What about your wife? – I have been a widower for three years. – You, a widower? Oh, dear me! – Yes, Madame. – Were you happy? – Happier than I deserved to be. She was a fine woman. – Oh, Edmond, I am glad to hear it. Poor Edmond, I congratulate you. You will be seeing my sister shortly. Let me tell her that you are here. As soon as I see her coming, please go into the other room with M. Molé – The pleasure of seeing her and you as well, Madame, is more than I could have hoped for. I may not have the strength to bear it. – She may also feel the same, but I shall prepare her and we shall see. – If only I could have seen my worthy friend again! – Ah, M. Rétif, I do not have that false modesty which would make me embarrassed were you to talk about him. Do not restrain your feelings. As the dear man was dying, your name was on his lips together with his children's. – That is the greatest comfort to me, Madame. – Do not call me Madame, call me Eugénie. Twelve years have been erased by your visit. No, do not call me Madame, it is a reminder to me that you should have called

me sister. – Kind and generous lady. Oh, I am overcome with
emotion. Before your worthy sister arrives, or whilst you are
waiting for her, tell me where . . . M. Molé will be kind
enough to direct me . . . (aside in the latter's ear), My dear sir,
I can bear it no longer, my heart is full and I'm afraid it will
burst. If *she* were to arrive now, I believe I would faint. Tell
me where I must go to visit our worthy friend. I feel the need
to unburden my heart in his presence. – I do not understand
you. – In which church does he lie and how shall I recognise
his tomb? Oh, what are you saying, Edmond? – Sir, dear sir, I
beg you to tell me. – Let us put it off, let us put it off. – No,
no, if it is in your power, please oblige me. – We shall be back,
M. Molé said to Eugénie. Prepare your sister during our
absence, and if you think it right that we should return, send
for us at Saint-Roch. We shall be near the screen.'

They set off, and on the way Edmond remarked:
'Our country women are for the most part kind and
virtuous, but I do believe, my dear, good sir, that the loveliest
women are to be found in Paris. Just consider the way they
talk, their kindness, their ease of manner together with their
pleasing appearance, their modest yet becoming dress. Oh,
what have I missed! But I did not deserve such great happiness.
Moreover, I obeyed my father, the living image of God on
earth. And I revere equally the one we are about to visit.
Dear and worthy man, he had the kindest heart, was virtuous and indulgent. He was faultless. Oh venerable Pombelins!'

The church was close by, and they entered as Edmond
finished speaking. M. Molé led him to the tomb of their
worthy friend, which was near the screen of a chapel. He
pointed it out, as there was no tablet. Griefstricken, Edmond
straightway prostrated himself and laid his cheek upon the
stone, but because his friend was present he made an effort to
stifle his sobs. At length, unable to tear himself away, he
begged M. Molé to return to Eugénie's and to send someone
to inform him if it were decided that he should not see Rose.

Once he was alone, he let his tears flow freely, and as the
church was empty, he accompanied them at intervals with
moving invocations to the worthy man whose loss he
lamented. 'Oh pure and holy spirit', he cried, 'look down

upon your friend from your abode in heaven with fatherly affection, I beseech you. Pour into a wretched heart the healing balm of comfort. Oh, if only you were still alive, one look would bring calm to my dejected soul.'

A respectable old man, who by the way he spoke appeared to be a dignified minister of long-standing, was praying in a dimly lit corner of the church. When he heard Edmond's voice, he got up and approached him. Hearing his footsteps, Edmond turned and bowed to him out of respect for his silvery locks. 'Come, follow me, my son,' the reverend priest said. 'I commend you for the way you express your grief. It shows that you have a good and upright heart. Come.'

He then led him to the foot of the high altar. 'If you have lost a father, my son, you will find here the best of all fathers. Put your trust in him, for I believe you worthy of it, and he will comfort you with his divine mercy.'

Edmond prostrated himself, whilst the reverend priest remained standing beside him and began: 'I was glad when they said unto me, Let us go into the house of the Lord.' When he had recited the whole psalm, the venerable old man embraced Edmond and withdrew. Edme R. felt comforted in body and soul, but when he looked for his comforter, he neither saw nor heard him. Deeply moved by the experience, he returned to the tomb. But now, instead of grieving, he gave thanks to God and invoked the name of his worthy friend who lay buried there.

A message was then brought from Eugénie that he should return to the house. Rose had been there almost an hour with her children, and Eugénie's husband, a good-natured man, had also returned. As soon as they saw Edmund, M. Bourgeois went to greet him and took him by the hand, as if he had known him a long time.

'I am most happy, sir, that I happened to return and can welcome you into my house, where I wish you to be as much the master as myself.' And as he presented him to Rose he added 'Sister, I held this man in high esteem long before I met him.'

Mme de Varipon got up, curtsied low before Edmond and offered him a seat beside her. Then, before saying a word, she pointed to her two children.

'Kiss them,' she said, 'you see how charming they are.' – 'Dear Children,' said Edmond, 'dearest children', and he repeated these words several times without adding anything. – I have heard that you have seven children. – Yes, Madame, – I gather that you are pleased with them. – Yes, Madame, very pleased. They are a comfort to me. – As mine are to me (pointing to her two sons).'

During these opening exchanges the others had got up and left the room, so that Rose and Edmond were alone together with her children.

'They told me you were at the church when I arrived. – Yes, Madame. – That was most proper, sir, and very much in character. You have not forgotten him then? – Forgotten him!'

As he spoke the tears began to flow and he could not control himself. Rose wiped them with her handkerchief, so as to hide her own eyes. – It is twelve years since you left us. He talked of you every single day. – (Edmond with a sob of grief) Oh worthy and respected man! we understood each other in our hearts. I thought of him every day, but who could I have talked to about him. – You never wrote to him. – Believe me, Madame, had he allowed it. – I understand. No one said anything to me about it.'

She caressed her children. There was a long silence which she finally broke.

'They have a worthy and honest father. As you know, he is my cousin. – Yes, I learned it today, Madame. – You remained in the church a long while, Monsieur. – I had a most fortunate encounter there. – What! Would you tell me about it? – Madame, I had . . . I was on my knees, overcome . . . a saintly man, a worthy priest came up to me . . . we began to talk . . . in the presence of God. He was a worthy, venerable old man, a tall majestic figure with white hair. He inspired respect, his words were a healing balm. You must know him. – No, I know no one in the parish of that description. – I assure you, Madame, he resembled the worthy man himself.'

Rose, seemingly seeking some means of distraction, called her sister to ask if she knew a priest in the parish like the one Edmond had described. Eugénie and her husband assured her that he did not belong to their parish. Edme R., already deeply affected, his imagination fired, thought it must have been M.

Pombelins himself who had appeared before him in this guise to comfort him. He said nothing of this to anyone, but the very thought of it coloured his whole face with an angelic, roseate hue, and the same idea seemed to communicate itself to Rose. For a moment they looked at each other in silence, then both rose to their feet and knelt down together. Edmond's exhilaration was shortlived, and reason quickly reasserted its control. But he confessed to us that for five or six minutes his belief had been total. As for Rose, he never knew what had passed through her mind as she said nothing to him, and he never saw her again.

'Monsieur R., I can now tell you what pleasure your visit gives me', said Rose after a short while. 'I was apprehensive about it beforehand, but I know now it has received approval. And that indeed is as it should be, my dear Monsieur. I shall return home now, and I shall expect you to come to supper with M. Molé and my sister's family. If you have any business, attend to it in the meantime. Goodbye until this evening. My husband will be delighted to get to know such a good man. He is already kindly disposed towards you, which is right and proper since I hold you in such esteem. I will leave you now.'

She departed with her children and climbed into a hackney carriage.

Edmond was overwhelmed. Eugénie, her husband and M. Molé were all present when the invitation was made, and they approved it heartily. Their guest then left to see to his affairs.

Having done his rounds, Edmond returned briefly to the inn where he was lodging and was given a letter which the postman had delivered during the afternoon. It contained news of a great calamity; part of the village of Saci had recently been destroyed in a fire. There were no further details. The accident had occurred after the harvest and the community was ruined. At first, the thought of what they had lost preoccupied Edme and filled him with sorrow. The note had been sent by his faithful servant, Germain, who was not used to writing and had kept it as brief as possible, without offering any explanation. 'My children', Edmond suddenly exclaimed. He hurried to a merchant, hastily did a deal with him for the rest of the wine, and set out the same evening. At Ponthierry,

on his way home, he remembered the supper and wrote a
letter of apology, which they received at midday the next day.
Until that moment their consternation had been considerable
and they had inquired after him at the wine wharf. At first,
they learned nothing, but at the third visit, they discovered
that Edme had set off at the news of the terrible fire. His letter
finally offered them an explanation. This was how he took his
leave of the virtuous Rose Pombelins and the lovely Eugénie,
for ever.

Respected ladies, you are no longer with us! But Edme R's.
children will unceasingly venerate and respect you, as if you
had been their mothers. I will say something about their
families at the end of this work, and I will also recount a
remarkable event which occurred in 1765, one year after my
father's death.

When Edme R. arrived in Saci, he found three quarters of the
villagers reduced to beggary, but his own house had been saved
as a result of Germain's zealous action and because of the way it
was roofed. He was not yet a judge, but he nonetheless made
every effort to relieve the distress of his fellow villagers. The
good priest, M. Pandevant, the predecessor of Antoine Foudriat who was at that time his curate, had over a long period
saved up the income from his inheritance as a dowry for his two
nieces, and he lived very strictly on his own emolument, which
amounted to no more than one hundred crowns. Witnessing
the disaster which had befallen his poor parishioners, he
generously sacrificed his savings, fed them throughout the
winter, and had their houses rebuilt as quickly and as well as he
could. He died the following year without having asked
anyone to repay their debt. Master Antoine Foudriat and Edme
R., who were aware of his generosity, waited until the
parishioners had reestablished themselves, at which point, in a
moving address he preached from the pulpit, the newly
appointed priest urged each of them to donate a certain sum so
that the nieces of the late priest, who were not rich, might
receive their inheritance. Though he had received nothing
himself, he set an example which Edme R. followed, and so
those who had suffered nothing in the fire gave even more
generously than those who had been helped. In this way, the
full inheritance plus the interest was restored to the nieces, with

an expression of gratitude and fulsome praise for the worthy priest they had lost.

The following year, a slanderous report about Antoine Foudriat was made by an unknown person to that respected prelate, Charles-Gabriel de Caylus, bishop of Auxerre, who with his chapter and the Order of Malta was lord of part of Saci. Edme R. called the villagers together at his house and begged any one of them to tell him if they had a complaint against the priest. As the response to his request was wholly negative, he suggested that they should send a deputation of twelve elders of the community to their pastoral leader on behalf of their own shepherd, who was much closer to them. The deputation set out with Edme as its leader and spokesman. The worthy bishop, who was a good judge of character, listened to Edme with such pleasure that he instructed him to return for a private audience, whilst his companions were dining in the servants' hall. Edme's conversation with the bishop lasted more than two hours. The prelate questioned him about the state of the parish, the conduct of the parishioners, in a word about everything which could possibly be of interest to a man who truly considered himself the leader of his flock. Edme's answers so pleased the prelate that he invited him to pay a visit whenever he came to town on business. Edme R. was all the more flattered by this honour, coming as it did from the man rather than from the bishop, and he did not fail to take up the invitation. On his first visit to M. de Caylus, the worthy pastor who had been told about the good deeds of the man from Saci spoke most kindly to him.

'Had I known you already, M. Rétif, your testimony on behalf of M. Foudriat would have been sufficient to redeem him in my eyes. If I can be of any service to you, do not hesitate to ask. Please believe me when I tell you that I shall serve you both as your spiritual father and as your friend in this world.'

I record this gesture because it was a special honour coming from such a man as M. de Caylus, and because my eldest brother succeeded my father in his warm affection. The worthy bishop was so kindly disposed towards the young priest from the moment he entered the seminary, that he offered to pay for his upkeep. Having refused a similar kind offer from the boy's grandfather, however, Edme R. was even less disposed to accept it from the father of all the poor. He told the bishop that by God's grace he was able to pay for his son's board, and that he would never forgive himself were he to take this money from the poor and the needy. M. de Caylus's respect for both father and son was greatly increased for the very reason which caused them to refuse this kind of offer, his love for the poor. For it is well known that the bishopric of Auxerre provided M. de Caylus with an income of between sixty and seventy thousand livres and that he distributed each year throughout his huge diocese more than eighty thousand livres. Yet he died leaving no debts, as they were all settled from the proceeds of a number of sales after his death.

Such a notable friendship did not prevent Edme R. from recognising merit wherever he found it, and he was in turn the close friend of two attorneys of the Jesuit order in Auxerre, fathers Scribo and Godo. These two men also consulted him about the running of their farm, La Loge, which was situated in the neighbourhood of Saci, and they received his disinterested advice with considerable gratitude. They sometimes engaged in disputes, but they were always conducted with such politeness on both sides that their close friendship was never threatened. On the contrary, father Scribo often addressed the following noteworthy remark to my father 'With your conduct, whatever views you hold are acceptable, do you hear, whatever views you hold are acceptable.' Father Scribo was himself an exemplary figure and most kind-hearted. He helped all those he could, and whenever it was beyond his powers, there would be such genuine expression of sorrow on his face that one went away happy, even though he had turned down one's request.

As for father Godo, although he was perfectly well-mannered, he was a little less popular. That was the result of his upbringing, for he was a gentleman and had been brought up proud-hearted, yet his friendship with Edme was as close as if they had been brothers. He in turn was dearly loved by Edme and whenever they met there was the same rejoicing in our household as on a feast-day.

Certain slightly overbearing people sometimes reproached

him with these friendships. Edme's only response was to invite them to one of their meetings at which he had the satisfaction of being warmly applauded. He was more flattered by the approval of M. de Caylus who, learning of what he had done on these occasions, told him that he was right to live in brotherly love with all men, and that certain other people would do well to follow his example for their own peace of mind and that of others.

Anne Simon, the worthiest of mothers, died in 1727. When she felt her end was near, she told her son to inform her three daughters. The eldest was married and living in Aigremont, and the two others were in Nitri. They were greatly upset by the news, especially Magdelon, to whom Edme was especially attached, as they were of a similar disposition. When they all arrived, Anne placed her son and Magdelon on one side of her and Catherine and Marie on the other.

'Dear children', she said, 'I am about to be reunited with your father. I live in the certain hope of seeing him in Heaven and I shall give him an account of his children's behaviour. May God bless you, my eldest daughter, together with your children. Though they are only daughters, see that they are good and gentle as well as hard-working. Gentleness and hard work are all that is necessary in a country household. Above all set them an example, now that they are growing up. Do you promise me that, Catherine?'

'Yes, mother dear.'

'Be good as well daughter, and see to it that your quarrels with your husband, however trifling, do not disturb my rest.

May God grant you children, Magdeleine. Mine have brought me such happiness that I want those I love and especially those I have borne to have them too. Comfort your brother after I am gone, and may he always see in you his mother Anne Simon who loved him dearly. Cherish your sisters, and if you have no children yourself, may you share theirs. And if there is no one to call you 'my dear mother', let them call you 'my dear aunt'. God bless you, my dear daughter.

Poor Marie, you are the youngest of my children. I urge you to behave responsibly and not to be a scatter-brain. You have a lively temperament, which is an advantage rather than

an imperfection if you can control it. And I urge you also to
respect your elder sisters and to look upon Magdelon, who
lives in the same village, as a second mother as far as you are
concerned. Promise me that you will heed her advice, when I
am dead.'

'I give you my promise, mother dear.'

'Dearest daughter, you are something of a worry to your
husband, but he is a good and honest man, and your son is a
sweet child, who already shows signs at a tender age of being
good-natured. Encourage these good qualities, my dear. A
son is like a second husband, but more respectful. Consider
your brother (may God always watch over him, amen). He
has been a support and a comfort to me in my old age. He will
close my eyelids, mourn my loss as greatly as he has loved
me; and he will reunite me with my respected husband, his
worthy father, in the same grave, just as he has always united
us in is heart.

Dear daughters, look at your worthy brother. Are you not
proud to be his sisters? Has he ever said or done anything since
he reached the age of reason which has not been to our honour
and advantage? Honour him with tenderness as your father's
successor. You know how he has behaved towards me, my
dears. He has not touched his inheritance, but has left it all to
me during my lifetime. Whatever he has is the fruit of his own
labour, and he has lived until this very day, this most precious
of sons, as if he had been born with nothing. I have been
greatly troubled, and it would have pleased me had he taken
what belonged to him. On the other hand, my poor heart
rejoices as I think happily to myself – I shall inform Pierre in
the next life how his worthy and respectful son behaved
towards his mother, and I shall thus increase his everlasting
happiness. This quiet and consoling thought brings me joy at
my death, as if it were a celebration. I am leaving my children,
but I go to rejoin their father.'

'I do believe that death is for you a celebration', said
Edmond, choking back his tears. 'Your heart has always been
full of kind thoughts and wishes and your hand has always
performed kind deeds. As for us, we shall be left, orphans of
the fondest of mothers, having lost already our glorious
fountainhead, our father.'

Looking at his sisters, who were weeping, he went on:

'Yes, let us weep, for we shall never again utter the words "father", "mother". They belong to us no more.'

'Come now, my son', (Anne Simon interjected with an engaging smile, as if she were still full of life), 'you will instead be able to say "my son", "my daughter", and these names are just as sweet. Let us give thanks to God, for life must end, and the most longed-for end could not surpass mine. May yours be just the same, dearest children.'

She died a few days later. Her body was carried the three quarters of a league from Saci to Nitri by her four children, who showed no false modesty in performing their filial duty. They alone bore their precious burden, followed by their children dressed in white as a symbol of their purity.

I have not omitted one single detail so as to depict true filial piety, which has been reduced to mere show in towns. Simple manners and customs such as these, which go back to the beginning of time, are more attributable to innocence and sound values than is commonly thought. Our present depravity is perhaps due to the disappearance of these ancient customs, or rather our depravity has caused these customs to disappear.

At the end of 1728, when he learned of the death of Rose Pombelins, Edme R. commented: 'I am still young and yet I already feel like old Brasdargent', alluding to those remarks of his which I recounted earlier. He went into mourning and wore it for two years in memory of both father and daughter.

In 1729 Edme R. became the steward of the three lords of Saci and administered the domain on their behalf. The increase in the number of responsibilites and the fact that his children were not yet old enough to work (his eldest son was in a seminary) led to his second marriage, which did not take place, however, until 1733.

Before coming to this period, I must introduce his second wife who, as is often the case, was not liked by her stepchildren, and who had no one to take her part in the community since she was a stranger. She was my mother, yet, in speaking of her with all the respect which that hallowed name demands, I shall nonetheless remain absolutely impartial. Happily, in order to praise her, I have only to make

known her daily conduct and the principal tasks she performed after her marriage. And this I can do without fear of
anyone contradicting me.

Barbe Ferlet de Bertro was born in 1703 at Accolai, which
lies at the point where the rivers Yonne and Cure meet. Her
father, Nicolas Ferlet, was a fine man who came from a very
good family. He was loved by everyone in the parish for his
integrity, his gentle nature and his goodness. His wife, my
grandmother, died very young, and he remarried. His second
wife was a kind-hearted woman who looked upon her
husband's two daughters as her own.

My mother was the younger of the two. She was fair-haired
and good-looking, but she had a lively even headstrong nature
which her upbringing did not curb. She was the spoilt one of
the family. Her father adored her, charmed as he was by her
good looks, and he forgave her everything. Her stepmother
was kinder and more indulgent than if she had been her own
child, and she even admired her dear Bibi's faults. And so this
youthful girl totally ruled the household whilst her elder
sister, who was more serious and sensible, had very little
influence. Later on, Bibi was to pay dearly for the fact that she
had had the upper hand when she was young.

The first set-back in her happy life resulted from an accident
which she caused by her own thoughtlessness. As Bibi was
gay and vivacious, she had lots of friends, and these young girls
used to gather at her house to spend the evening together.
Anyone who flattered Bibi was welcomed by her parents.
Besides, her father enjoyed having these young people around
him, paying their respects to his daughter, who outshone
them all. One evening in the autumn, they had stripped a lot
of flax and swapped many amusing stories. Bibi, who was
extremely tired and anxious to turn in at once, could not be
bothered to put all the stalks outside. Despite her sister's
remonstrations, they went to bed. They had only been asleep
a short while when flames suddenly started to shoot from the
pile of stalks and set fire to the house. M. Ferlet and his family
escaped in their nightclothes, saving only their lives. This
accident reduced their circumstances considerably, and they
never recovered from it. Their house was destroyed together
with their furniture, which though old was very fine, their

linen, their clothing, their deeds, their silverware. They lost everything. M. Ferlet was so distracted and so griefstricken that he was incapable of attending to anything or of saving the remainder of his possessions. He mortgaged his land in order to rebuild his house.

His own greatest sorrow as well as his wife's (they often said) was that Bibi had caused the accident, and she was inconsolable because of it.

There were further repercussions of this terrible stroke of fate. As M. Ferlet's fortune was reduced, a certain Mme Pandevant, who was also a Bertro and very rich and extremely fond of Bibi, asked her parents if she could look after their daughter. They grieved and they wept, but in their own dear daughter's interest, they were obliged to send her away. And so they let her go, and she went to live with her relation in Auxerre and then followed her to Paris, where she lived for two years.

It was here that Bibi's pretty face and lively temperament attracted a number of admirers. All those who met her fell for her, but she was capricious and mocked their sighs of love; and if ever she showed any interest in them, it was only for the money they might have brought her.

Amongst their number was a handsome, well-to-do and good-natured man of about forty-five whose family was well-known. Suddenly on one occasion he declared himself her suitor. Bibi found him to her liking (she was looking for an established household) and asked him to speak to Mme Pandevant. She was delighted at the prospect he offered her protégée and welcomed him as a suitor. The marriage was arranged in eight days. Immediately after the ceremony, the married couple went to live in the provinces. Bibi, who was now Mme Boujat, gave birth to a son who was sent by her husband to a wet-nurse at Pourrain, ten leagues from where they lived, even though there were wet-nurses in their neighbourhood.

One day, after M. B. had set off very early in the morning to visit his son, so he said, his young wife was visited by a woman in her fifties. Her demeanour, though gentle and kind, commanded respect. She asked for M. B. – He has gone to the country, Madame. – Has he gone far, Mademoiselle? – Ten leagues from here, Madame, to see our son who is with a

wet-nurse. – When will he be back? – He usually stays several
days, since he also has business to attend to. – Have you been
married long? – Eighteen months, Madame. — How did you
get to know M. B.? – At my cousin Pandevant's. She arranged
the marriage. – Ah, it was authorised by a relative, that
changes things. – In what way, Madame? Forgive me for
saying so, Madame, but it changes nothing. – You have a son?
– Yes, Madam, he is a sweet boy. I have only seen him once,
and I long to see him again.

The lady sighed deeply.

– Dear me, Madame, do forgive me, I didn't ask you to sit
down. Do you know my husband, Madame? – Very well
indeed, I assure you. – I am pleased to hear it. He is a kind man
and I am well contented. He is most considerate towards me.

The lady sighed again and tears filled her eyes.

– I believe you, Madame. You are young and attractive and
you have borne him a son. – Oh, if you only knew how much
he loves him. He worships his son and talks of nothing else. –
I believe you, I believe you, Madame. Had you known M. B.
long before you married him? – It was all settled in eight days.
– In which parish is Paris? — S. E.. Would you care for some
refreshment, Madame? – No, Madame; someone is waiting
for me. – You have someone with you? – Yes, Madame. – It
would give me great pleasure if you would do me the honour
before leaving . . . – It is not possible.

As the lady answered her, Bibi whispered something in the
cook's ear, and she went out to ask the three people who had
remained in their carriage at the door if they would care to
come in. They were three of the lady's relatives. The strange
looks they gave Bibi, whom they addressed as Mademoiselle,
did not cause her a moment's reflection. But what should she
have thought? Could she have imagined the misfortune
hanging over her head? Moreover, she was such a scatter-
brain that she never noticed anything or paid any attention to
the looks people gave her.

The lady whispered to the three men for some considerable
time, reporting her conversation. It was not very polite, but
Bibi meanwhile was serving them some light refreshment. It
is still the custom in the country to show this kind of
hospitality, which people in olden days were renowned for and

which was absolutely essential. It is only spoken of with wonder in Paris as a strange or outdated custom.

After the lady and her friends had had a brief discussion, they left without offering any explanation.

Bibi, who was now alone, thought about what had happened and was greatly surprised. Her servant then told her that the four people had talked heatedly as they got back into their carriage and that the lady had said: 'She had accepted everything in good faith, what do you want me to say? Let us keep the whole affair secret, my dear friends, in God's name, let us keep it secret.'

The unfortunate Bibi was even more surprised by these remarks, but she had no reason to reproach herself, and she tried to set her mind at rest until her husband arrived.

He should have been away for a week, but he arrived the next day before noon. He was rather anxious as he came in, but, realising from his wife's greetings that she knew nothing, he regained his composure.

'I have to go to Paris, my dear, on most important business', he said. 'We shall leave tomorrow, so you must get ready. I have things to see to myself.'

As she prepared for the journey, Bibi told her husband about the strange visit she had received the day before. From the description which she gave him, M. B. realised that it was his wife, for he was already married. He had fallen passionately in love with Bibi, whom he had seen in Auxerre, without ever having spoken to her, had followed her to Paris, and, having assumed the name of one of his brothers who had died many years earlier in the New World, had married the object of his passion, and then taken her to the village of Saci. It was well off the beaten track and yet convenient for his business, and had seemed a safe retreat. There, he readopted his real family name, by which he had never been known either in Auxerre or in the surrounding district. He had grown disenchanted with his first wife for a number of reasons. Firstly, she was older than him, and secondly she had not borne him the child for which he had longed. Lastly, he was the victim of love, that overwhelming passion, which, when it flies in the face of virtue, always brings untold troubles that cause one's downfall.

Thus they prepared to set out for Paris. But that same evening, at the dead of night, there was a loud knocking at their door, and a servant went to open it without waiting for any orders from his master. He leaped out of bed as soon as he awoke and armed himself with two pistols. Immediately he opened the bedroom door, he was confronted by his wife and her three relatives. He was dumbfounded. The men reproached him vehemently and made violent threats. His wife was crying. The unfortunate Bibi, realising from this scene the awful situation in which she had been embroiled, was in despair, all her hopes dashed. She was ambitious, and ambition alone had impelled her to get married. No amorous young man had ever touched her heart. Picture her in her predicament. She appeared half-dressed before the lady and threw herself at her feet.

'I am innocent in the eyes of the whole world', she said, 'even in God's eyes. Yet you think me guilty, I can sense it. Forgive me the wrongs I have committed unwittingly, but do not confuse innocence with crime. I don't ask to keep your husband. Simply grant me the favour of not dragging me with him before the magistrates, so that my name will not be on everyone's lips. My poor father would die of grief. Spare his grey locks and my youth.'

As the lady lifted Bibi up, she embraced her. And Bibi's tears were so powerful that they mollified the three men, despite their great anger (what can beauty not achieve!). They ceased their abuse, and everyone regretted what had happened and began talking with each other. The lady struck up a friendship with her rival, which became so intimate once she got to know her well, that she almost adopted her as a daughter. Had the law permitted it, she would have allowed the marriage to stand, so sincere was her friendship. It grew stronger still when she had seen the child. In wanting to take care of it herself, she revealed the same fine character as Queen Elizabeth of Portugal, who raised the children of the king's mistresses. Nothing was known about Bibi's shameful marriage, and the unfortunate girl placed herself in Mme Boujat's hands and lived with her as if she were her own mother. The secret was even kept from M. Ferlet. But one can be sure that M. B. saw neither his legitimate wife nor the one he had deceived.

Mme B. died two years later, and, as a mark of her genuine affection for Bibi and her son, she left them all she could, including real estate. M. B., now a widower, made approaches to Bibi through Mme Pandevant, to whom she had returned with her son. The lady advised her ward to accept the proposal, which she did. Thus she married M. B. a second time and lived happily with him (as he still adored her) until his death in 1732.

No sooner had he died, than greedy collateral heirs prepared to reveal the shame of young B.'s birth. His anxious, worried mother was represented as having been a willing concubine. I would relate all the horrid details, were I not her son.

Mme B. confided her sorrows to Master Antoine Foudriat, but the young priest didn't trust himself, dealing alone with a young and attractive woman, and he wanted Edme R. to be present at their meetings. The young woman told her story, which she confirmed with letters written by the first Mme B. and by several members of her husband's family who had grown attached to her, and especially one close relative of M. B. who lived at Chitry. The priest and the judge, a position which Edme R. then held, came to respect her greatly and helped her all they could.

But the heirs' relentless attack upon the pretty young widow could not be curbed. Adored by her husband, she had often treated them somewhat haughtily during her lifetime. Now, they thwarted all the priest's attempts to prevent a scandal. One day, in desperation at their stubborn persistence he took Edme R. by the hand and said:

'My dear friend, we know her as if she were our own sister. These people will hound her to death, which is what they want. You are a widower, I urge you to marry her with all her rights. The esteem in which you are held will impress these wretches, and your high reputation for fairness will silence all the vicious rumours. She will owe you respect, and you will gain a charming wife who will make you happy. You are too young to remain single for ever. It is a heavy burden for someone as steady as you are, who has never suffered loss on account of any excess. Now you know my feelings and what I ask of you as your devoted friend. I am placing you, Madame, in someone else's care', he told the young widow, 'but he is such an honest man that I am sure that you will not oppose my choice.'

On this occasion Edme R. was the most embarrassed of the three. He saw before him, almost at his knees, a pretty, tearful woman whom he could rescue from countless difficulties. Compassion is a powerful force in a generous heart, and his friend urged him warmly to agree. He did not refuse, but asked for a little time to make up his mind.

'I will give you twenty-four hours, only because it will cause no delay', the priest told him. 'The banns can be read on Sunday, a dispensation granted for the other two readings, and you shall be married at four in the morning on the first possible occasion.'

After their discussion, Edme R. left in a pensive mood. Seven children! but that should have worried the young woman, not him. Out of generosity, however, he resolved not to take her for his wife, but to do everything in his power to help her. He even talked to his father-in-law about her. Thomas Dondaine was most alarmed at the very idea of marriage. He thundered against it, and the next day he drew up an inventory in favour of his grandchildren. Edme R. did not appear concerned at this action. On the contrary, seeing his children's rights secured and considering the advantages to his own fortune and their's which might result from a second marriage with a woman who had numerous title-deeds, he went back to the priest less inclined to turn down his request.

As soon as the priest saw him, he took him aside and wouldn't let him go until he had his consent. The terms of the marriage were drawn up and the ceremony was held on the day which master Antoine Foudriat had appointed.

The outcome of the marriage was as favourable as the priest had supposed it would be. All slanders ceased, the heirs became more accommodating, and there was no law-suit as everything was settled by the lawyer.

Once married, Edme R. realised he had done the right thing. One cannot imagine the disorderly state his household was in. There was no underwear, table linen etc. Since the death of his good mother, he had enjoyed none of the comforts of life, and, left to fend for himself, he had experienced a certain uneasiness and sadness which had gradually affected his health.

Whilst he busied himself securing her estate, his new wife restored order and prosperity to his household. She wanted to assert her authority over his grown-up daughters, who had become used to being independent, but she was unsuccessful in this as a result of faults in her upbringing. Never having been contradicted, she doubtless went too far, but only after they exceeded all bounds with her. However, her husband was not in the least aware of these family quarrels. Whenever he appeared, his wife recovered her composure and complained only on rare occasions. Someone else had to inform the head of the house what was happening in his own home. That was after I was born, for I am the first child of my father's second marriage. Other children followed almost without interruption with the result that in 1745 Edme R. had fourteen children, eight girls and six boys, all of whom were living. And when young B. was at home, there were fifteen of us who could address them as mother and father. It is strange that the same number of children was born to each marriage. The only difference is that there were two boys by the first and four by the second.

One of my father's sisters (Marie, the youngest) happened to spend several days with us on one occasion. The first two days everyone restrained themselves, but the patience of the elder daughters gave out on the morning of the third day. They were in the wrong and my aunt, suprised at their outburst, took her sister-in-law's part against her nieces. But that was not the way to restore peace. The girls cried and said that everyone had deserted them since this fine lady had arrived and stolen their father's heart. And for the next few days, the same scenes were repeated. So my aunt, who was by now convinced that these people could not live together and were only making each other unhappy, spoke to her brother about it.

'That is what I foresaw', he replied, 'and I congratulated myself too soon that I had happily been mistaken, but I have a solution. It is the older girls who are the cause of the trouble. I have received a proposal of marriage for my eldest daughter. It is a good match, but I was hesitating. I shall now accept it. The second wishes to go to town as an apprentice. She can go. My father-in-law, Dondaine, has asked for the third and I will give her to him. He already has the fourth. I shall keep the youngest who is gentle by nature and still only a child. As for my two sons, I am unaware as to whether their sisters have won them over to their side. In any case, the eldest, who is a grown man despite his youthfulness, is in a seminary, and the younger one is on the point of going. Moreover, he has such a fine character that I have nothing to fear from him. These arrangements are quite straightforward. But, believe me sister, had the circumstances been different, I should have spoken up as father and head of the house and brought these young people to their senses. They abuse my goodwill. Tell them that had Pierre Rétif still been alive (may God grant him peace) and learnt of their behaviour, he would have come here, even at his age, and dealt with them in such a way that they would have trembled with fear. He wouldn't allow his daughters to express any feeling or opinion, or to assert themselves before they were married. They were not even allowed to say 'yes' or 'no'. Tell them this, and tell them also that I shall adopt his attitude when I talk to them. Warn them, sister, I beg you. It would not be in their own interest to tolerate their resentment, and my children are too precious for me not to mind their faults.'

The young people were told firmly what he had said, and they trembled with fear. But Edme R. still carried out his plan, and as a result peace was restored, once and for all.

The next day, after his sister had spoken, he assembled the whole family, and addressed each one of his daughters in turn.

'It was only yesterday that I learned of the scandalous disorder which prevailed in my house and of such marked insubordination that no one accepted my authority. Had I chosen a beggar's daughter to act on my behalf and exercise my authority, I would have expected her orders to be obeyed with respect and without any argument, even if she had only been a servant. But you challenge my own wife, part of me; you dare to question my choice. And what are you? mere girls, from whom one expects modesty and obedience. What I should do at once is make such an example of you that any impudent hussy who didn't know her place would be scared stiff, because that's what you deserve. But I am restrained by the pleas of the very person you have had the audacity to

insult. You, Anne, don't bring shame upon your grandmother's name (may God protect her). And you, Marie,
whose smiling face should reveal a kind and gentle heart, take
care lest I deal still more harshly with you. Your wickedness is
wilful and not some fatal weakness you've inherited. I might
have made allowances for your thoughtless character, Mar-
ianne, had the excesses of your conduct not matched your lack
of consideration. Yet, though you are more headstrong than
your sisters, you did not go as far as them. How sad a father's
lot is, when he is reduced to praising one of his daughters for
being less blameworthy than the others. As for you Magdelon,
you scarcely emulate the aunt whose name you bear (may God
bless and keep her). I wanted you to be present and to hear your
father's justifiable reprimand, even though you have been
living with your grandfather, because it has come to my ears
that you have spoken to several strangers against your father's
chosen partner. It is an outrage, and I would never have
imagined my own flesh and blood capable of such a thing. To
my horror, it would seem that I have harsh masters and stern
judges in place of children. With what terrible disfavour they
have viewed my conduct! And even if they haven't dared utter a
single word, what have they thought of me? I hope that my
sons have not been party to this abominable act of revolt. But if
I learned that they had, they would feel the full weight of their
injured father's indignation, and their punishment would hor-
rify you, you impudent creatures. If anything gets back to my
ears in future . . . ! Since you appear to want a tyrant in place of
the loving father I have always been, a tyrant you shall have.
You stupid girls, if you had to deal with Pierre R. (may God
bless him for ever), where would you be? Ask your aunt, there.
But you wouldn't have made the same mistake, if you had had
such a father. Every day I give thanks in admiration for his
wisdom. His stern justice is what your unruly sex almost
always needs, for you are the stubbornest of creatures. The
more you are indulged, the bolder you become. On your
knees, all of you, at once, and beg our forgiveness for your
crimes. Let me never have to repeat . . .'

His stern look was enough to make the four proud girls drop
to their knees, and their aunt recited to them the apologies they
had to make. But they had scarcely begun, when their step-

mother pushed her husband aside and came forward to embrace them and to help them up.

Nothing was said by Edme R. to make his daughters reflect upon his wife's generous action. He withdrew, leaving them alone with their step-mother and their aunt. This is what took place on that occasion. But Edme R. had too good an understanding of the human heart to count on any long-term peace, and so, without further delay, he implemented the plan I have outlined. The frenzy of activity surrounding his eldest daughter's wedding kept them all in line and occupied them for a couple of months. And then the departure of his second daughter for Paris provided a further distraction.

As for his sons, seeing that they were destined for the ecclesiastical life, Edme R. believed that it was not proper to raise the issue of the few wrongs which they had committed in lending their vocal support a little too keenly to their sisters' cause. He respected the purity of mind and heart which ministers of religion must have. And, since they were men, he could not have avoided entering into certain details with them about the necessity of marriage, a husband's obligations towards his wife, the union which exists between them and which is so strong that they become as one, as well as about the love which they share as man and wife. Nevertheless, he reserved the right to speak his mind when they had reached maturity, in the firm belief that a good priest, if he is to intervene in family quarrels and restore peace, has to know certain things which he can only learn from an upright, married man.

BOOK 4

What follows is, one might say, an account of my father's *patriarchal life*. I shall consider him in his role as family man, as judge and as head of a parish, which, in the way it was governed, resembled in many respects the republics of old.

Léonard Dondaine, Thomas's nephew, who was a simple peasant, and had never heard of Caesar or of the Romans, used to say: 'It is better to be first in Vaudupuis than last in Paris.' The most important person anywhere is always respected for his position, and only foolish townsmen (the worst kind of all) and unprincipled brutes would despise him.

The little parish of Saci together with its communes is governed like a large family. Everything is decided by majority decision in the assemblies which are held in the square on Sundays and feast-days after mass, and which are announced by the ringing of the large bell. It is at these assemblies that the parish appoints its officials, whose functions are something like those of Roman Consuls, its tax-collectors, its constables, who watch over the newly sown fields and the vines, and finally its public herdsmen. The man who presides over these assemblies represents the lord, whose procurator fiscal also brings forward matters for discussion. But each individual has the right to expose any abuses which he knows of or to put forward useful propositions which he has thought of. These matters are discussed forthwith, and if they are of any importance the village officials are sent to the subdelegate of the Intendant for them to be authorised. It is also at these assemblies that the section of common woodland that each person can cut down is allotted every year. Lots are drawn, except in the case of the priest, the head man, when he lives in the village, and the two public officials, to whom the thickest sections are allotted. But since my father's death, neither the judge nor any of the law officers live in the village. All of them are from Vermanton and are thought to be more educated. Might I here deplore the fate of a parish which is delivered into the hands of these quill-driving strangers, whose only interest is in creating dissension. It would be a hundred times less dangerous if the peasants themselves, who are believed incapable, were entrusted with these charges. They are perfectly aware, as my father was, of each other's means, and any law-suit is fully understood before the lawyers for the two parties have their say. It would be impossible for them to take in a local judge on any matter. I shall say no more, but this querimony (as it used to be called) will serve as a transition, leading me on to the way in which Edme R. administered justice.

He knew the means of the parties involved, their way of thinking, and the motives which determined their behaviour. It was on the basis of such knowledge that he always sought to reconcile them. He did his utmost to achieve this end, but when he failed he allowed the law to take its course, and he followed it to the letter. No personal motive governed his actions, only the proper formalities and sound law. Furthermore, not one of his judgements, throughout his long magistrature, was ever quashed; or if it was by the bailliage of Auxerre, he had the satisfaction of seeing the good judgement of his initial decision upheld in the decrees of the high court. His success, which was never denied, won him the singular respect and confidence not only of his fellow parishioners, but even of those of the surrounding villages. As a judge he never gave way to pity, but as an ordinary citizen he was quite different. A young attorney, the son of his nephew the procurator fiscal who subsequently became a famous advocate in a court of appeal, used to plead his cases with a great deal of emotion when the circumstances permitted. Once, having taken on the case of some poor fellow who had been deprived of his inheritance by a rich bourgeois from Crevan, he roused the feelings of the court, and even the judge shed a few tears. Yet the poor man lost his case and had to pay costs. The rich man produced a valid title-deed, whereas the poor man had lost his, he said, in the fire which I have already mentioned.

When the sitting was over, the judge invited the stranger to dinner, and he also asked the priest, master Antoine Foudriat, the procurator fiscal, and the young defence lawyer who had lost. Edme R. was convinced, deep in his own heart, that the poor man was in the right. They had dinner, but at the end of the meal, the poor man who had lost his case was sent for in order that they might grant him some delay in settling his costs, which were not considerable. The stranger, who was moved by what he witnessed, refused to accept what was owed him and signed a document to this effect. The poor man was then sent away.

As soon as he had left, the judge asked the stranger who had won the case if he might have a few words with him in private. He expressed his doubts concerning the legitimacy of the man's victory with such force that he shook him. But the inheritance was advantageous to him and this alone prevented him from acting justly. And so he departed. The priest, the judge and the procurator fiscal together decided to buy at their own expense a small piece of land next to one of the poor man's fields and to give it to him as a form of compensation. They carried out their plan at once, as the judge was a solicitor, and sent for the poor man to come and sign the deed, without revealing to him the source of this gift. As a result, he thought that the man who had seen fit to forgo his expenses had also performed this splendid act of generosity. Believing this to be the case, the poor man set out the next day, full of gratitude, to thank the bourgeois of Crevan, taking with him a small gift of game and poultry. The rich man was surprised at what he heard and declared that he had had no part in the purchase of the land. Realising, however, the source of the gift, he wrote straightway to his métayer in Saci, instructing him to hand over another field of the same size to the poor man and to let him choose one he liked from all the land he owned. This was done and the poor man had two fields instead of one, and he became the friend and protégé of his opponent in law, who constantly helped him thereafter.

One is conscious of the fact that it is impossible in large towns for judges to know every individual, but it is an advantage in the country and we would humbly beg every lord of a parish to encourage it. Less learning and more integrity would be most expedient in the lowest courts. Moreover, as the judge and the procurator fiscal belong to the community, they keep an eye on everything, so that corrupt practices are either forestalled or quickly checked. I will return now to the case which I was describing.

When everything was settled, the young orator was complimented, and his father congratulated him on this occasion for having followed Edme R.'s example. And he cited one of his uncle's speeches for the defence when he was only procurator and maître Boujat, his predecessor, was still judge.

The case concerned a mother who was pleading against her children to be allowed to keep the whole of her late husband's estate. The request was unfair. But Edme R., whose intention it was to move these children and to make them search their hearts, took on the case and prepared a speech on the subject of what children owe their mothers. Being such a good son himself, he spoke from the heart, as one can imagine; and at that time he was treating his own mother exactly as the widow wanted her children to treat her. First of all, he painted a touching picture of the mother's tender feelings for her two sons and her daughter when they were small. He described the hardships she had undergone in order to bring them up after the death of her husband, how she had worked night and day, which was common knowledge, how she had deprived herself of necessities so that they would not go without, and he gave examples which everyone knew of and which moved the court to tears and won their admiration as well. The judge, who was so overcome that he could not control his feelings, exclaimed from the bench:

'One moment, one moment, Maître R., you are laying snares in the path of justice. Right is on the children's side, even if nature and reason are on the mother's side.'

'What is right is what nature and reason dictate', retorted the young procurator, rather sharply.

The judge ordered him to be quiet.

'Allow me, sir, before you give your judgement', Edme R. said, 'to address these children for one moment, who are, it must be said, hard-hearted, in order that I might try to arouse their feelings towards such a loving mother, who, bowed by the burden of her years, asks those who are in their prime for the means to support herself, just as she once supported them. She asks only for her daily bread, which she will water with her tears if what they give her is too hard.'

These words, more moving and more powerful by far to the peasant than townsfolk can possibly imagine, drew forth sobs from everyone in court. Only the children remained dry-eyed.

'You have won your case', exclaimed Edme R., 'you have triumphed over a . . . mother; what a sad and unhappy victory! But in the name of humanity and in your own interest, do not take advantage of her. Do not drive this unfortunate woman to despair, who has shown you so much love! . . (taking her by the hand and leading her forward) what must she do? Must she beg for mercy? And will she obtain it from you? (seeing them still unmoved). 'Unhappy woman', he cried, 'you have borne tigers in your womb not human beings, and today they tear you to pieces. Come to me, come to me, I will be a son to you. As for you, you wretches, tremble, tremble with fear! Yet, you need not fear your mother's curse. Your venerable mother is too tender-hearted and still has a blessing for you on her lips. But your retribution will be all the more terrible. I see, I see already God the avenger using the hand of your own children to visit it upon your heads.'

He uttered these final words with such force that everyone present let out a startled cry. The unyielding children were shaken at last. They embraced their mother and withdrew all their demands there in court, promising to give a formal undertaking before all their fellow citizens that they would leave her in full possession of everything, without let or hindrance as long as she lived.

Edme R., having recovered a little after such a forceful expression of his feelings, apologised to the judge and to everyone gathered there, and even to the children for his final remarks, which he admitted were a little strong. But the judge embraced him, everyone applauded, and the children themselves thanked him.

Then, in the presence of the procurator fiscal, the clerk and a few other officers of the court, Edme R. said quietly to the judge:

'Sir, I knowingly defended a case I should have lost. I will bear the costs, whatever the amount. Send me the order to pay, without this poor family knowing anything about it. This has been my intention since the poor woman came to me about it.'

Such was the account given by the procurator fiscal of his uncle's noble deed. The priest praised him, the young lawyer was happy to follow at a distance in his footsteps, and the worthy Edme was moved to tears. This deed reminded him of his esteemed father and dear mother, and it was for them that his tears flowed.

'Children', said Antoine Foudriat to the little family group assembled there, 'love your father and your mother and you will be truly virtuous. You will love God and your neighbour, which is the whole law, as Jesus tells us. Love and honour your father, for in him you have the model and example of an honest man.'

I have referred briefly to these two positions which my father held, that of leader of his community and of judge. However important these titles are in the eyes of a good citizen, they are less interesting, less common than that of family man. In this capacity Edme R. was perhaps the most outstanding example of his century. As his son and as the historian of his life, may I be forgiven for expressing myself in these terms. However, I hope that the reader will share my admiration or that he will at least excuse and understand it when he has considered all the details I shall give him.

Fellow-citizens, I shall paint a picture of an everyday kind of virtue, an easy and amiable virtue which provides the only solid foundation for happiness in this world and for one's reputation after death.

Having curbed the spirit of anarchy which was beginning to show itself amongst the children of his first marriage, Edme R. lived happily with his new family. All his labours had secured him a degree of comfort, and the reputation which he enjoyed was deserved. His eldest children, both boys and girls, were in good health, and he was cherished and respected by his wife, as Pierre had been by Anne Simon.

Every evening at supper, which was the only meal at which the whole family could meet, he saw himself as a venerable patriarch at the head of a large household. There were usually twenty-two at the table, including the ploughboys and vine-dressers, who acted as threshers in winter, the herdsmen, the shepherd and two female servants, one of whom helped the vine-dressers whilst the other looked after the cows and the dairy. They all sat down at the same table, the head of the family at one end near the fire, his wife next to him within reach of the serving dishes (for she alone took care of the cooking, and the servants who had worked all day long sat down and ate their meal in peace). Next came the children according to their age, which was what determined their position, then there was the longest serving ploughboy and his companions, the vine-dressers, and after them the herdsman and the shepherd. The two servant girls completed the group, and they sat at the other end of the table opposite their mistress, who was thus able to observe their every move.

Everyone ate the same bread, for in this house the odious distinction between those who had white and those who had black bread did not exist. Moreover, no saving would have been made, as the slightly coarser bran was needed for the horses, the dairy-cows, the pigs that were being fattened, and also for the sheep when they had lambed.

Since the head of the house consumed little wine and had begun taking it late in life, he only drank wine that was mature. His wife drank only water, which her husband persuaded her with some difficulty to redden slightly with a few drops of wine. All the children without exception drank water. The ploughboys and vine-dressers drank a wine which they enjoyed much more than they would have done their master's. It was a wine made from the second pressing, using the marc of the grapes. Everybody knows that peasants in general like a wine which rasps their throat, and this taste is particularly pronounced in Saci, where the human animal is of a massiveness and a crudeness scarcely ever seen elsewhere, even in Germany. Germain, the principle ploughboy, had a truly teutonic appearance. He was a huge man with a long face, which, though it wasn't fat, was at least six inches wide; and he gave the appearance of having incredible strength. In spite of this, he had a friendly and reassuring expression, which meant that the children were always looking for him to play with them. After the master and the mistress, Germain was the most respected member of the household. The other servants never did anything without seeking his advice, which

he always gave without appearing overbearing. What an
excellent fellow he was, and how lucky those households are
which have such workers. How lucky too, good servants are
whose masters truly appreciate them. The herdsman and the
shepherd, who were usually young men, showed respect to
the ploughboys and to the vine-dressers. The two servant
girls were helpful to them all, and they had been asked by their
mistress to mend the men's undergarments and their other
clothes. There were also fixed times at which the two girls
could do things for themselves.

Edme R. had been unable to set aside certain hours in the
day-time for prayers or even for meals. The duties of all the
wage-earners were completely different. It was only at breakfast, at five o'clock in the morning, when nearly all of them
were there, and in the summer the herdsman and the shepherd
had already gone to the grazing-grounds. They prayed
together briefly, saying just the Lord's prayer, and then they
went their separate ways, only meeting up again in the
evening. At that time everyone was present. It was therefore
after supper that the head of the house read from the Bible. He
would begin with Genesis, reading with great spiritual feeling
two or three chapters, depending on their length, which he
would accompany with a few brief observations that he
judged absolutely necessary. It is with considerable emotion
that I recall how attentively everyone listened to that reading,
how it communicated to the whole family (and I include the
servants in the family) a mood of goodwill and brotherly
love. My father always began with these words: 'Let us collect
our thoughts, my children, for we are about to hear the word
of the Holy Spirit.' The next day at work, the readings of the
previous evening provided topics of conversation, especially
amongst the ploughboys.

At this point, I must make an observation, which I have
already made in *L'Ecole des Pères* (tome 1, p. 264), namely that
those who plough are better behaved than those who tend the
vines, even though their work is harder. It is also true that
herdsmen are inferior in this respect to vine-dressers, and that
shepherds are not so pure and simple as herdsmen.

In summer after the reading, they said a short prayer
together and the young ones were asked to recite a lesson

from the catechism they used in the diocese. Then everyone
went to bed in silence, as laughter and conversation were
strictly forbidden after evening prayers.

In winter, when the evenings are longer in the countryside,
(time never seems to alter in town), the head of the household
told stories, sometimes old ones and sometimes new, after the
reading and the lesson from the catechism. And he would
introduce, when appropriate, the loftiest maxims of the
ancients. That was our recreation. These instructive tales were
eagerly awaited, and, as everyone could laugh and talk about
them, they provided delightful entertainment for the peasants
and children, who had never heard anything so enjoyable
before. These conversations and the readings must have given
them great pleasure. We often had the sons of the most
respectable people in the district as servants, and when their
parents asked them why they were so keen to be part of our
household, they always mentioned the reading and conversation in the evenings. Had my father been politic enough to do
this deliberately, it would have been very shrewd behaviour
on his part.

As far as the day's work was concerned, the head of the
household was indefatigable in his activity, setting an example
above all by his deeds rather than by telling people what to do.
Never was there a better master or one more loved by those
who served him. The main reason for this was that service
was mutual, whenever the occasion presented itself. This
saying of Solomon's was always on his lips: 'If thou hast a
servant, let him be unto thee as thyself; entreat him as a
brother', and the following as well: 'Whereas thy servant
worketh truly, entreat him not evil.' He got up at day-break
and drove one of the ploughs himself. He was such a good
ploughman that his lads had only to copy him, but not one of
them, not even Germain, could claim to be his equal. He was
proud above all of this one skill, and one could see by the slight
smile which came over his ever-friendly and gentle face how
flattered he was when someone told him he was a good
ploughman. 'It is the art of arts', he would sometimes reply.
'One can pride oneself a little, if one excels at it.' He hated
working on the vines and only spent any time on his own
when the grapes were harvested. Being a good master

however, he would go and look at them and knew perfectly well if anything was amiss. This dislike of his was not a fault. Had he enjoyed working on the vines, with all his other occupations, lawyer, magistrate, adviser and arbiter, he would have had to give up ploughing which he loved above all else. He was never idle for a moment except on Sundays and feast-days. Even then, he had a book in his hand if he went walking alone, and this would be a moral work or law book, in which he was studying some passage or other relating to a case on which he had to pronounce judgement during the week. He used to say that his *Praticien français** was an excellent devotional book since it taught him his duty.

He was always approachable as far as his workers were concerned, but a little more reserved with his daughters, whom he never addressed in the familiar manner.

With a view to creating as many bonds as possible between his first and second families, he made the older children godfathers and godmothers of the younger ones. The worthy priest of Courgis and the eldest daughter, Anne, gave me my names, and so on down to the youngest, to whom I was godfather in my turn, the youngest daughter of the first marriage acting as godmother. This was in 1745 when my father was fifty-three.

The following year, Edme R.'s prosperity, despite the fact that he had fourteen children, alive and well, to look after, roused the envy of an inhabitant of Sacy, who was a collector of taxes. He raised my father's taxes to an exorbitant level, at which Edme complained mildly, but no one paid any attention. Irritated by this, perhaps too much (this was his own view), he felt he ought to take advantage of the law in favour of fathers having twelve or more living children. He presented a request to M. de Brou in Tonnerre, who was at that time the local Intendant, simply drawing his attention to the facts and without making a complaint against anyone. The administrator wrote in his own hand: 'Edme R., father of fourteen children, six livres', and informed him by word of mouth: 'You should pay nothing at all, but since you have asked to be taxed, I have fixed it at that level, and it will remain the same

---

* An old treatise of jurisprudence.

each year. I know, moreover, that you are too loyal a subject of the king to wish to be entirely exempt.'

A few years later, M. Berthier de Sauvigni having succeeded M. de Brou, the same envious people put Edme's share of tax back up to its former level. He went back to the Intendant with a three line request and immediately received the same reply as he had done from M. de Brou. M. Berthier asked him to appear before the whole assembled gathering, as he wished to show them the father of fourteen children. He spoke affectionately to him and, patting him on the shoulder, congratulated him on his happy fatherhood. Throughout his life, my father was taxed at six livres by the Intendant himself or by his subdelegate.

This detail, which truthfulness obliges me to report as it happened, may appear surprising on the part of a man who thought as Edme did. Perhaps I might be allowed to offer an explanation of his motives. He was consulted on tax matters as he was on other public affairs. There are, however, in every parish a few trouble-makers who like to create opposition and to show how powerful they are by doing wrong. In spite of Edme R.'s observations and those of the wisest inhabitants, it happened all too often that the poorest people in the parish were over-burdened, either on account of particular dislike for them or because they were thought to be less hard up. Edme R. and the priest, Master Antoine Foudriat, were in the habit of secretly helping these poor people by paying their tax. The reader can now see that, by being overtaxed himself, Edme R. was no longer able to contribute to the relief of his poorest fellow-villagers.

My account of his life as a husband would certainly be less than complete if I said nothing of his wife's conduct, especially as a father and mother together form one whole being.

Edme R. always preserved a certain marital dignity with both his wives. He did not address them familiarly, nor was he addressed by them in this manner. He always assumed a respectful air with his wife, without either affection or stiffness. His wife, for her part, always addressed him with due regard. It is true that his own behaviour and the way others regarded him were sure means of winning her esteem. I am not well informed as to the details of Marie Dondaine's life, having acquired only the most general views about her. As far as my mother is concerned, I know much more, since I was an eye-witness of her behaviour.

I have been told that in the early days of her marriage, her extreme vivacity and the indulgent upbringing she had received meant that she did not always choose the surest means of winning her husband's affection. With any other man she would have been unhappy, but Edme R., who was a wise and prudent husband, studied his new wife's character and behaved towards her in such a way as to influence her way of thinking. He prevailed upon her feelings, trying to persuade her first of all to curb her vivacity a little. Then he firmly instructed her as to her true obligations, but in private, so that no one in the family suspected what was happening. On the contrary, in front of the children and with strangers he showed her the greatest respect. This is part of the advice he gave her, which my mother recounted to me herself after my father's death. She told me about it so that I would realise how much she owed him and how nothing could possibly diminish her sense of grief at his loss.

'My dear wife, the most dangerous fault in a husband is to be weak and not to bear the sceptre of marital authority. It is a fault I noticed in Parisian husbands. I want you to be happy, and I would not have married you, had I not had in mind our common interest. But it was not something I wished for blindly. I perceived how I might achieve it when I first decided to give you my promise. It was indeed my very aim in marrying you, that of being your helpmeet and defender. But a helpmeet and defender is not a slave. Tell me, where does a man acquire the strength which nature has given him? Why is he, moreover, always a free agent, bold, courageous, audacious even? Is it so that he shall fawn like a feeble admirer? Why is it that nature has given you such charm, made you weak as well and fearful? Why has she given you such a soft-spoken voice, with such delicate and endearing inflexions? Is it so that you can give orders harshly and haughtily? No, my dear wife, it is so that you can be beguiling, so that you can, in a word, sway your stronger partner and win him to your side. Your lot is to please the one with whom you are joined, and who is as one with you, and, with your gentle caresses, to ease the burden of toil which he undertakes on your behalf. That charming smile exists only to bring him instant distraction from his labours and to encourage him to undertake others that will be still more arduous.

If a wife finds her husband weak, she gives orders and believes she is happier as a result. But she is simply domineering. And although wielding authority gratifies one human passion, it does not bring happiness. Indeed, it is a passion which sets one at odds with one's fellows, creating more trouble than true pleasure. Keep to your role therefore and never err from it. I am no tyrant, but if you do not do as I say, I shall assume your role, and however ridiculous I might appear with my masculine features and bushy beard, you will have to bear with it until you allow me to assume mine again. You smile, but I assure you that I am serious in what I say. The first principle of a happy marriage, without which all the others are valueless, is that the head of the house should give the orders and that his wife, to whom he shows tender affection, should do for love what anyone except a wife would do out of obedience.'

'You are sugaring the pill, but I understand what you mean.'

'It is for that reason that I have spoken clearly, my dear wife. One should always make oneself clear. Don't tell me that you were happy in your first marriage, based on entirely different principles. Your first husband wronged you totally from the start, and then believed that he should do everything in his power to make you forget it. I approve his conduct in that respect. It was wise, and I would have done the same thing in his place. But our situation is different. We are no longer children who have to delude each other. We are a mature couple who should act responsibly, each fulfilling our role to the full. It is only by obeying nature that one can be happy. The natural role of the stronger sex is to govern, the natural role of the weaker and fairer sex is to temper any harshness he may show not only to her but to the whole family as well. I am firmly resolved, my dear wife, to conform to the will of nature. Be gentle, win what you can, but do not make demands. Moreover, your authority over the household is as great as mine, since husband and wife are as

one, but you are not the head of the family. Since there are
two of us, one must lead. The one to whom nature has given
the power to impose his will by force must exercise it in
response to the deference which is shown him. Then he can
give the credit to the one who has renounced it in his favour
and exercise his authority as a friend and father-figure.
Regulate your life from now on according to these principles.
If it were merely a question of my own happiness, I would
willingly make sacrifices to you, sure as I am of my own
strength, but I know from experience that wives who play at
being husbands are the unhappiest of all. Women resemble
oriental peoples, having something of their lively and easily
disturbed imagination. Without realising it, they prefer
authority which they must obey without question to one
which they can choose to obey or not at will. Since they are
always indecisive, they would spend their lives in a wearisome
state of perplexity. What is more, if one took away from
Asiatic people their despotic leaders, they would find others
the next day. I read somewhere that the Romans had this
experience with the people of Cappedocia, who preferred
absolute rule to freedom.'

'But, my husband, I do not ask to rule you.'

'Nor do I, my dear wife. All I ask is that both of us should
know our place and that there should be harmony and
agreement between us such as exists between the parts of one
body. Listen to me. Every time you want to do something,
put it to me in a disinterested way and I will consider it calmly
with you. If it appears beneficial to us both or only to you, it
will be settled without further ado.'

'I give you my word.'

Barbe Ferlet, who initially had been quite an ordinary wife
on account of her particular circumstances and her upbringing
as a spoilt child, became a veritable Anne Simon for the rest of
her life. The nightly readings from the Holy Bible gave her a
true sense of her obligations, and I was thus able to witness the
touching spectacle of my mother bringing to life again the
wifely conduct of a bygone age. It is impossible to describe
every tiny detail of respectful behaviour which bears witness
to subordination in a wife without however suggesting servitude. But it is always pleasing to the eye of a stranger, because

he knows that it is nature's way, which every individual would like to follow.

The more submissive and attentive his wife became and the more she treated him as her beloved master, the greater the consideration Edme R. showed her. Strict as he was in having her feared and respected by the whole household, he had made clear in one of his inviolable rules that, whilst he would willingly excuse any insult to him personally, no one could expect any indulgence whatsoever if they had been disrespectful to his wife. And this is what happened one day to one of the female servants who deliberately allowed an excellent bitch and a favourite of Edme R.'s to die. Everyone was afraid for her, knowing how attached the master was to such a useful animal, but he saw fit to reproach her mildly and in such a paternalistic manner that she wept with regret. A month later, the same girl lost her temper with her mistress and was extremely rude to her. When Edme R. heard about it, he dismissed her at once and would not listen to any excuses or even the pleas of her mistress.

Then, addressing my mother, he said: 'Wife, if I allow anyone to be disrespectful to you, you will soon find the whole household in uproar. You know that the best way people can pay me respect is by respecting you. Whoever shows you a mark of esteem pays me a double compliment, and a single act of kindness done for you is worth ten that anyone might perform for me. The same is true of our children. I am much more gratified by a kiss given to my son or daughter than by a great demonstration of affection towards me. Why (and I ask you to forgive the example, but I can think of none more apposite), why is a man so sensitive to a smack given unjustifiably and for no reason to his dog? Why is it often enough, in order to win his friendship, to give the animal a stroke or a piece of bread? It is because his master sees in this gesture a sincere desire to please him. This is a poor illustration. A favour done to one's wife or one's children is dearer by far to a husband's and a father's heart.'

Is it surprising that such a husband should have been held in high regard by his wife and adored by his children? Moreover, he was the inspiration of his household, absent as well as present. Everything that was said and done was related directly to him. If he was away on a journey and happened to arrive home a little after supper in the evening, all the family, children and servants, awaited his return worriedly and anxiously. If he knocked at the door, the very sound of the knocker brought forth shouts of joy from everyone in the house. And I never heard that knocker strike without seeing my mother tremble with delight. She would get up quickly, repeat her orders to open the door, even though five or six people were already there. She busied herself, got him his night-cap and his clogs (these are worn as slippers in this region), which she filled with hot embers, even though her daughters wanted to do this for her, placed his chair in his favourite corner and poured him a glass of mulled wine, which she would give him as soon as he entered before even saying a word to him. The patriarch drank with an air of contentment. Then he greeted her and the rest of us as well, down to the shepherd-boy, inquiring as to how everyone was in a kind and friendly manner.

Alas, that was true happiness! I only ever knew it there. What a hapless creature I am to have sought it elsewhere.

He would then recount to us the news he had heard, whether in Auxerre, in Vermanton, in Noyers, Tonnerre or Vézelai. One can imagine how avidly we listened, living as we did in such an isolated village. If someone had to go out whilst he was giving us his news, it was clear how sorry they were to have to leave. But when the person returned, Edme R, was considerate enough to repeat what he had missed. He went further with the servants. If someone called during the day, as often happened, and had brought some news or said something useful or unusual, he would share it with everyone at the evening gathering. But accounts of this kind never interfered with the Bible reading.

Every evening during Advent, as he had a very pleasing voice, he used to like singing carols which, as everyone knows, are simple songs. They provided recreation for the family which he made extremely pleasurable.

Thus our good and wise father, who was strict about everyone fulfilling their obligations where work was concerned, did not consider it beneath him to take charge of our daily recreation. 'Pleasure', he used to say, without having read Young*, but it is such a natural thought, 'pleasure is the balm of life and only innocent hearts give themselves up to it completely.'

One evening, an unusual incident occurred which showed how beloved he was of all the inhabitants of the village. An individual from Nitri called Balton, who had stayed drinking in Saci until nightfall, thought it would be a good joke as he returned home to shout 'murder'. He was on the hill, at the foot of which La Bretonne is situated. Unfortunately, my father, who had gone to Nitri, had not arrived home. Hearing the stifled cries uttered by the drunkard, my mother almost fainted and called all the servants who had not yet come in for supper. They armed themselves and set off, and my mother sent to the village for further help. As soon as it was known that Edme R. had been attacked, everyone left their supper, picked up whatever they could find near at hand, and rushed along the main road to Nitri. They found no one. The drunkard, hearing such a crowd approaching (there must have been at least five hundred people), jumped into the vines to hide. The villagers continued on their way and would have reached Nitri had they not met my father, at the corner of the common woodland which belongs to that village, returning home peacefully. He had been rather suprised by the noise he had heard coming towards him, and as soon as he could hail those who were closest, he called out to them: 'Hey there, my friends, what is it? What's the matter? Has some mishap occurred in the village?' They explained the reason for the commotion. He thanked them from the bottom of his heart, and when he reached home, he tapped the best barrel he had, and the small army soon drank it dry.

This adventure was much talked about in the district and retold in different ways. It was known that Edme R. was carrying money home, having done the rounds of his debtors, and everyone believed, and perhaps still does, that he really had been attacked by Balton, but that he wanted to spare him by concealing his crime. For my part, I have told the truth.

---

* Edward Young's *Night Thoughts* were translated in 1769 and became extremely popular in France.

Having talked of Edme R.'s conduct with his wife and servants, it only remains for me to describe the way he behaved towards his children.

He was strict without being hard, and the irrefutable proof that it is the best method is seen in the fact that the children of his first marriage, with whom he was much stricter than those of his second marrige, for the most part turned out better. A further proof is that the eldest children of the second marriage, who were treated almost as severely as their elder brothers and sisters, have a stronger sense of moral values than the younger ones. I am trying to be impartial and as impersonal as I can be in order to convey the truth. In his old age, however, he was excessively indulgent. It was yet another mark of virtue in this respectable old man. But the Rétifs tend to be too immature by nature for such a regime to be beneficial to them.

However, he never showed any severity towards his eldest son who, because of his happy disposition, had shown a propensity for goodness even as a child. Indeed, he carried it to excess, showing that he was 'restive' in something (this was one of the lawyer Rétif's expressions), and it was only a question of tempering it. Such was Aristotle according to Plato. What a blessing a son like that is to his father, if the happiness he brings were not tinged with fear at the thought of losing him.

As for the younger son of the first marriage, I never heard anyone say that our father had to treat him harshly. Yet he was lazy, and his excessive kindness, from which all those who knew him were to benefit so greatly, might once have been seen as a fault had it been carried to excess. Moreover, he wasn't liked by Thomas Dondaine, his grandfather and godfather, who was entirely won over by the shining qualities of the eldest boy. But Edme R. encouraged his second son and would often show his special affection by saying to him: 'Thomas, as I loved my father more than myself, God has in his wisdom inspired me to entrust my eldest son to him, in whom divine goodness is rekindled, but he has entrusted my second son to me, in whom I am pleased to recognise myself. Be good, dearest son, intelligence is a dangerous attribute if it is not sufficiently blended with goodness. You will be happier, even if you are less distinguished. Let that be a consolation to you, dear Thomas.'

I am the eldest child of the second marriage. I have the same features as my father and eldest brother, though I am less handsome than them. As for my character, it is infinitely inferior to my father's as regards his goodness and the moral strength which won him such esteem, and it is equally inferior to my brother's in terms of his intelligence and understanding. I am a mis-shapen monster and I bemoan my birth, knowing that I am as unworthy of the family from which I come as of the example which I have been set. Forgive me, oh dear departed father! Forgive me too, oh worthy eldest brother who has taken his place for me! I shall redouble my efforts to live up to the name which we share.

Jean-Baptiste R., the second son of the second marriage, died at fourteen. His intelligence was limited, but he might one day have been a second Thomas R. His artlessness and kindly disposition were the delight of the whole household during his childhood, without him ever being spoilt as a consequence. Our father, who laughed at his naivety, would not have permitted that.

Charles R. is the third son. He was the living image of my father in looks and cast of mind. But he was resourceful and spirited. In a word, he had Pierre R.'s wits and our mother's liveliness in Edme R.'s body. This child who showed such promise was killed at Hanover in 1757. He was in the Auvergne regiment and was only seventeen.

Pierre R., the youngest son, looked after the family home. His upbringing, as I have already implied, showed the effects of our father's indulgent old age. This son died on August 5th 1778, leaving seven children, four of them boys. I would simply add that we have received good reports of his eldest son's feeling for husbandry and his instinct for thrift and hard work. Yet this child is still only twelve years old. May he follow in the footsteps of Edme R., and so bring him to life again in the countryside which he served so long and so usefully.

When one of us had done something wrong, he was immediately reprimanded with some severity, yet not punished on the spot. But my father straightway decided upon the punishment to fit the crime, sometimes taking away our privileges, sometimes giving us the cane. Punishments

were announced several days in advance and each day the
guilty one was reminded of his sentence. If it was the cane, it
was put off for eight days and was announced after the initial
reprimand in this manner: 'My son so-and-so (or my daughter
so-and-so) in eight days at such and such an hour you will be
caned by me (or if it was one of the girls by her mother) to
atone for the crime you have committed and to serve as an
example to your brothers and sisters.' The announcement of
the caning was only made once. But at the appointed time, the
guilty person was summoned and his conduct from the time
of the sentence reviewed. If it had been good, he was
pardoned, if middling, he was lightly caned, but if he had been
bad, he was soundly thrashed. I once had a thrashing like this
from my father and I could still feel the effects of it a fortnight
later. Needless to say, one couldn't run away. But one had to
have done something very serious to be given the cane. I only
had it twice and I was exceedingly naughty. Most of the other
children, especially the two eldest boys and the girls, never
received it.

But when a child had done something which deserved
praise, he duly received it in the evening in front of the
assembled family, as befitted his action.

For example, one of the boys was commended for having
given a poor man his dinner of bread and milk and a fresh egg,
which had been brought to him in the fields where he was
watching over the wheat which had been spread on sheets to
dry. For this he received his father's blessing.

Another was praised for having bravely driven off a number
of fat cattle which were spoiling someone's crops, thus
sparing him further loss and the owner of the cattle a fine and
the cost of the damage. This child was only eight.

Yet another of the boys was recommended, if slightly less
ceremonially, for having at the age of ten fought off a wolf
which was attacking his flocks. With one hand he had boldly
snatched the prey from its jaws, whilst beating it with an
iron-shod stick he was holding in the other. The wolf was
finally driven off when those who had witnessed the fight
were able to come to the boy's aid.

A daughter was solemnly praised for having restrained the
band of reapers who were making vulgar remarks to a pretty

young girl who was gleaning the field and for having allowed the poor creature to eat with her, so that they might treat her with more respect. To show how repugnant he found the harvesters behaviour, Edme R. made a touching ceremony of it and thereafter allowed the girl to be a reaper and to earn as much as the rest of the band.

In his youth the worthy eldest son, Edme-Nicolas R. had been praised on numerous occasions for illustrious displays of charity, modesty and filial piety towards his parents.

The eldest daughter, Anne R., who was already married, was commended for her behaviour at home towards her very wayward and idle husband, whom she had transformed with her gentleness, her kindliness, the encouragement she had given him; and also as a result of her incredible eagerness to spare him some of his labours by doing as much as she could herself, and sometimes more.

Marie R., though absent and settled in Paris, was praised for her conduct in that city, according to the reports of her mistresses and one of her aunts. As she was pretty, she had had several nasty experiences which she had come through with as much modesty as courage.

It is unnecessary to point out to the reader how much such truly patriarchal behaviour helped to develop high moral principles. Even those of us, unhappily hurled into the hurly-burly of a corrupt city, who succumbed for a few wild years to dangerous pleasures, before long searched our hearts and returned to those sound principles which had been instilled in us in childhood.

There are many details which I must omit for fear of them becoming excessive. I believe, however, that the worthy citizen to whom I owe my life will now be better known.

Finally, Edme R. received the title which he had so longed to merit, that of 'good man'. Every day he would hear people use it, but one evening he chanced to overhear a conversation between Jacquot Blaise, the shepherd, and Germain, the ploughboy, which must have given him great pleasure.

J. B.: Tell me, Germain, what does it mean when people talk about our master as a 'good man'? Germ.: Don't you know already what it means? Jacq.: I have an idea, but I don't really know. Germ.: Do you know what being a good father

is? Jacq.: Yes. Germ.: A good husband? Jacq.: Yes. Germ.:
Good to one's neighbour and God-fearing? Jacq.: Yes. I know
what that means. Germ.: Well then, that's what a good man
is. Jacq.: Now I know. Goodness, he really deserves it. Our
master's just like you said, Germain.

After supper that evening in front of the whole family, the
'good man' said: 'There is one legacy I should truly like to
pass on to you. I hope that wherever you go and whenever
you say you are my children, everyone will reply "Ah, you
are Edme R.'s son, he was a good man". Believe me, my
children, that is worth more than if one were to say he was a
rich man, a skilful man, a clever man. He defeated an army on
his own, and the king made him an earl, a marquess or a duke
or whatever it might be. As long as you all live, my children,
and for the rest of your life which you have only just begun,
have one aim and ambition, that of richly deserving this fine
and useful title; for if you merit it, it will finally be granted
you.' 'As it has been in your case', said Germain. 'For
everyone gives you that name, and especially those of us who
are closest to you, and from whom not the slightest thing is
hidden.' 'May God be praised for it, Germain.'

Here is yet another illustration of the keen and pure delight
which the title 'good man' gave my worthy old father.

One of his sons, who was living in Auxerre at the time, set
out to visit his father with one of his friends the day before All
Saints. About half-way home, they passed through a village
where a close relative lived. Following a recent youthful
escapade, however, young R. was badly received, and he was
humiliated at being treated in this way in front of his friend.
So they set off together at once along lanes that were
overhung with trees in places. They had only covered half the
distance when they were overcome with fatigue and hunger.
The two young lads, who were both about sixteen, had very
little money. In particular, young R., who had never experienced the need for it, had neglected to bring the ten or dozen
two sou coins he had. They were rusting away back in his
room with some other small change. And so they were
obliged to knock on a door as they passed through Puits-de-
bond. They found the good peasants at table, enjoying a
supper of pickled pork, and there was a jug of wine in front of

the fire. Three families had gathered together to celebrate the
end of sowing. Each family served as helpers to the others,
that is to say they joined forces to make up a ploughing team
with three horses.

'Could we have a drink please, which we'll pay for?' asked
the ravenous lads. – To be sure, gentlemen. Sit yourselves
down by the fire. One must make room for new arrivals. –
But we don't have much money, said young R., and his friend
pulled two and a half sous out of his pocket, which was the
sum total of their wealth. – There's enough there for you to
feast on, said the peasants, laughing. Sit down at the table and
put you money away. You don't pay in advance here. Might
one ask where you have come from? – From Auxerre. – And
you set out as late as this! – You can see we're not afraid of
robbers, said R's friend. And we should have spent the night a
league and a half from here at my friend's brother's house, but
he showed us the door.

Young R. blushed and kicked his tactless friend under the
table. 'I've got to do something to get my own back', his
friend replied, 'but I'll keep quiet about it to your father.'

The young lads began to eat, not with the appetite of
sixteen year olds, but with the restraint of those who only had
three sous and one liard to spend on their meal.

But the head of the house was studying his two guests
closely. Young R.'s face especially seemed to strike him.
'Gentlemen', he said at last, 'without wanting to be inquisi-
tive, may I ask where you are going. – To Saci. – I'm not
mistaken, he said to his friends, they are his sons. What are
your names? – I'm called Rameau, said the friend, and he's
called Rétif. Hearing this name, the whole table suddenly rose
in a state of great excitement. 'So you are M.R.'s son. Why
didn't you say so when you came in! Oh, what a good father
you have. There isn't an inhabitant of Puits-de-bond to whom
he hasn't done a good turn, and he's been especially kind to
me. Wife, fetch the black pudding. We couldn't enjoy it in
worthier company, unless his father were here, that is. Come
now, gentlemen, you can't leave tonight. Here is a bed for
you. The whole household was in a state of confusion, and
young R's friend, who was a small and lively chap, was
overjoyed. At every turn these people exclaimed to each

other: 'Oh, what an excellent father, you have.' And to Rameau they said, 'Young man, your friend would be welcomed everywhere in the neighbourhood as he has been by us.' 'I am not surprised you attach such little importance to money', said Rameau to his friend, 'you have no need of it on your travels. Come now, I'll forgive you for the reception we received earlier and the escapade that caused it.'

Finally, the two lads got ready to leave, even though their hosts tried to put them off by scaring them. As they departed, everyone drank to Edme R.'s health and blessed his name a thousand-fold.

In less than two hours the lads reached Saci, even though it was almost three leagues, but they had been restored by the food and wine which the good people had given them. They arrived just as R.'s father was finishing the Bible reading. It was the chapter in Genesis where Jacob, returning from Laban, meets his brother Esau and manages to gain his favour. This touching story had moved everyone, and they greeted the son of the house with great joy, even though he was also scolded a little for arriving so late. His friend was also welcomed in a proper manner. Their appetite was almost as keen as it had been at Puits-de-bond, and so they were given some supper, and the whole family stayed to listen to their account of their journey, for the young stranger had already referred to the difficulties they had encountered.

Once they had eaten, R.'s father said to them: 'Come now, my children, tell us about the misadventures you met with on your great journey which you've now completed.'

'Don't mock us, sir', the young stranger replied, 'we really did have misadventures, and they were most unpleasant. Worst of all, we ran the risk of dying of hunger. We left Auxerre at nine o'clock – Did you lose your way then? – Indeed, we did. – What's that, my son, don't you know the way yet? – The fact is, the stranger went on, we kept to the side-roads, and they were certainly that alright. By six in the evening we hadn't eaten a thing, and what we'd had in Auxerre could hardly have been called breakfast. On top of that, we had no money on us. Had I known what a good credit-note your son is. – Credit-note, what do you mean? – And a valid one, sir, your name. As soon as we'd given it,

bread, wine, meat, an excellent black pudding, a good fire,
greetings almost as affectionate as those we received here, all
this was heaped upon us. I have never witnessed anything like
it before.'

Without drawing breath, the young man told them everything that had happened at Puits-de bond. Each time he
repeated the phrase the good people had exclaimed almost like
a refrain – 'What a good father you have' – the old man could
be seen raising his eyes heavenwards, scarcely able to hold
back his tears.

What a delightful moment this was, and were this virtue's
only reward, would it not surpass all the supposed pleasures
which vice procures?

I shall now draw this interesting story to its close, but I will
add a few details of my elder brothers' conduct, which will
complete my portrait of the virtuous father who produced
such children.

Edme R. enjoyed quite good health until 1763, when he
contracted the illness from which he died in 1764. In that
year the rains flooded the meadows, and when mowing time
came round the worthy old man, who had never let anything
keep him from his work, still believed himself to be as
invulnerable as in his youth (may I be forgiven for saying
this). He himself cut the grass under water with a skill which
he alone possessed, and he managed to save the best part of it.
The water was so cold that all those who helped him fell ill as
a result, and my youngest brother had an extremely high
fever. But the most serious effects were suffered by my father,
who had worked harder and longer than anyone. A slow fever
gradually took hold of his sturdy body and weakened it
perceptibly over a period of almost two years.

I haven't had occasion to mention my mother's eldest son in
the course of this work. He practised an art which is as useful
to mankind as it is noble, to judge from the manifest and sure
relief which it brings, that of surgery. And he achieved
distinction. He understood my mother's and my father's
constitution so well that he always treated them successfully,
whether because his method was infallible or because their
confidence in him was more important than the remedy, I do
not know. This splendid fellow died when he was twenty-six

as a result of a fall from a horse, and he left a young widow who gave birth to their son after his death. Throughout his painful illness, all that Edme R. ever said was: 'Oh dear, if only poor Boujat was here.' That was the only complaint he made.

Master Antoine Foudriat was no longer alive and so a young priest administered the last rites. He had such a profound respect for the old man that he honoured him with special ceremony. He was accompanied by the whole parish. The old men, in tears, filled the sick man's bedroom, and everyone was on their knees in the courtyard offering up a prayer for his well-being.

After he had urged upon the congregation the necessity of preparing themselves in advance for death, he went on, addressing himself to God: 'O Lord, I have prepared a place for you this day in the worthiest of tabernacles. The soul of a good man is, in God's eyes, the most fitting temple there is. Take courage, oh worthiest father (for out of respect, he himself told us, he would not call him brother), for either our prayers will be answered or you will enjoy everlasting life in the bosom of Abraham with the righteous, of whom you are one. But of all the righteous, none can expect a more glorious reward, if I may venture to say so, than a good father, who has raised each of his children in the paths of happiness and virtue, who has provided the church with worthy ministers, the country with brave defenders, and the state with worthy citizens at every level and above all with exemplary and faithful mothers. There will be songs of joy in heaven as you enter, and the holy patriarch Jacob together with the earliest saints, whom you revere, will lead you to the throne of Him that Is.'

An exhortation such as this was much to the liking of the venerable old man and it drew tears from his eyes. From that moment on, he awaited death with serenity and even with joy, troubled only by my mother's grief.

He is no more! Almighty God, your noblest creature is no more! For a virtuous father is truly created in your holy, living image. May God bless you, oh my father, and from your abode of righteousness, look down with favour upon your unhappy son. Amen.

Truth compels me to utter just one reproach against this virtuous man. He wanted his children to get on in the world, and only one was brought up to work on the land. He looked after our education as much if not more than his means would allow, intending us to live in the capital. Without doubt, this was due to the high opinion which the virtuous Pombelins had inspired in him for such a dangerous place as well as to the advantages which he himself might so easily have enjoyed. But just as keenly as he wished to see us settled in Paris, he strove equally strongly to dissuade us from setting ourselves up in some provincial town. And he would often repeat the following argument in order to dissuade us.

'My children, man's nature is so good that he must do everything he can not to harm it. Now, there is nowhere in my experience where that fine nature is more debased than in a small provincial town. Five or six wealthy inhabitants behave as if they owned the place and seem merely to tolerate the useful members of the population who cultivate the land, practise a trade, or run a business. On occasions, I have witnessed revolting examples of such behaviour on public walks from these would-be men of property, who, once they have acquired all the principal legal offices, have all the power in their hands. I should die of grief in such a place. In Paris, on the contrary, a man is freer than he is here. There is only one master and he is the same for everyone. And if a duke or a peer casts a slur on your name, you can at once return the insult. That is the great and happy consequence of the liberty one enjoys in such a vast city, where one not only observes the whole nation in all its majesty, but where the human race breathes the healthy air and precious fragrance of equality. Whenever I have glimpsed Paris from a distance, I have had the warm feeling of a son revisiting his mother. She is, to be honest, a somewhat capricious mother and sometimes rather hard, but most of the time she pampers her children to the point of spoiling them. I will say nothing of the pastimes and amusements one finds in Paris. This huge city offers an unending spectacle, in which the scene changes every instant and with every step one takes. But best of all, she is like an ever-open book which one can browse through all day long, if one has nothing else to do, as one wanders along the quays past the sellers of old books. You will also see engravings of the greatest moments in history, and if you have a little learning you can improve your mind as you stroll or go about your business. At every turn, you can help your neighbour, without dipping into your pocket if you haven't much money. And you can practise your devotion at any time as you go on your way, for, in Paris, God is worshipped at all hours of the day and night. In addition, the human body, on which so much care is lavished, is as a rule as fresh as a rose at dawn, before the dew has dried in the warmth of the sun and the dust of the day. Even finery, which I don't condemn, lends to certain faces an air of good humour and contentment. The women are ten times more attractive than elsewhere. Paris, then, my children, or our own village, but rather Paris than our village.'

Nothing could be truer than the good man's feelings on this score. I myself have experienced everything he said, and the picture he paints of the capital, which he considered a refuge for the oppressed and the consolation of the human race, is one of those strokes of genius which one understands better than one can express it. But there are many risks to morals! Alas! is vice inherent in the capital, or does the person who is corrupted there not bear the seeds of corruption in his own heart? Edme R. lived as pure a life in Paris as in his own village. Oh happy mortal! Oh happy country which only produced children such as you!

My father was not mistaken in his prophecy that the capital might be advantageous to his children. Had it not been for unfortunate circumstances, two of his sons would have found the same happiness as their father. Charles R., who died as a soldier in Hanover, was befriended by a Parisian lawyer who was so delighted with his fine qualities that he proposed to marry him to his niece one day. We still have the letter which he wrote to my father on this matter after the young man had enlisted. His enlistment was not caused by libertinism, but was the result of a sudden burst of enthusiasm which gripped him and inspired him to serve the State, by risking his own life.

Another son might have been happier still, but this unhappy wretch has always been dogged by adverse fate. What a sad example he is of the undisciplined child who gives way to tempestuous passions and demands to have his own way in the most important decision of his life, that of marriage. Before recounting his adventure, we must tell the reader of the unusual circumstances in which he found himself.

In 1764, by one of those striking but not extraordinary coincidences, one of M. Pombelins's grandsons by his daughter Eugénie happened to be in the same business and to have achieved a similar fortune. He had two very pretty daughters, the elder called Rose and his younger Eugénie after their grandmother and great-aunt. By another coincidence, one of Edme R.'s sons saw the girls without knowing who they were and fell head over heels in love with the elder one. Carried away by a passion he couldn't control and with no clear aim in view, since he was already married, this ill-fated young man wrote anonymous letters, in which he declared his feelings with such force and such sincerity that they made an impression not on the young girl herself, but on her father. He wished to know who could possibly write such things, and he gave his employees orders to try to take him by surprise. They were successful after the tenth letter, catching him not at the moment when he delivered it, for the young man was too careful, but as he was revelling in the pleasure of watching the beautiful Rose at a low window. They seized him and dragged him inside, where the two young girls, their brother and the rest of the family were, though their father was out at the time. What an embarrassment for a person who was timid by nature and very untidily dressed. He suffered considerable humiliation, but the cruellest affront of all was the disdain of the girl he adored, which was however richly deserved.

The head of the household returned just as they were making him write a few lines, in order to convince themselves that he was the author of the letters. As soon as M. B. saw the young man, he sent everyone away without exception, experiencing as he did so a keen and heartfelt interest in the stranger. He then spoke gently to him:

'Why do you seek to awaken in my daughter's heart a passion that can only cause her frightful torment? Why do you show such disrespect to me, since I have done nothing to harm you? Try at least to justify yourself with some explanation for your behaviour.'

The imprudent young man was so overwhelmed by such good will that he threw himself at M. B.'s knees. – I have done no wrong, he said, that is all I can and wish to say. I was carried away in spite of myself. My crime is not wilful. – That is the customary excuse of all those who do wrong. – I am desperately sorry for what I have done, but I am too honest to deny that I would do it again, were the opportunity to arise. – Who are you? – A young man from the provinces. – From which one exactly? – Burgundy. – Burgundy! What is your name? He told him. – Let us talk quietly together, my good friend. Did your father ever stay in Paris? – Yes sir, and he was more fortunate than I. – Did he not know a M. Pombelins? – Oh yes, sir, very well I assure you. — Very well! I am angry at what happened, but come back again tomorrow and make yourself a little smarter. I have something to tell you. I presume you are unattached, a bachelor that is, and with no ties of any kind. Goodbye. Go out this back way. Everyone has gone now. Come back tomorrow and ask for me, do you understand?

The young man departed in a state of despair. And the next day he hadn't the courage to show himself. He was not unattached. He wrote to M. B. giving him the gist of what he had to say, and begged him to offer some encouragement.

Reply.

You know my name. I am Eugénie Pombelin's son, and I have heard about your father from my mother and my aunt. I would be delighted to carry out a long-standing project, assuming that is that you take after your father, as my elder daughter Rose takes after her aunt and my younger daughter Eugénie after my mother. We shall expect you this evening. Eugénie Pombelins, who is still alive, is really looking forward to meeting you.

R.'s reply.

Sir, a demon who destroys my peace of mind drove me into your neighbourhood. I shall not visit you. I cannot, but it will kill me. I am truly yours.

The young man did right. What could he have achieved? But he was embittered for the rest of his days. Unhappy until then, he felt his troubles grow, his health declined, and he came close to death. And even though his strong constitution enabled him to pull back from death's door, he never recovered his peace of mind, let alone his happiness. Condemned to everlasting self-reproach, he was justly punished for the crimes he had committed against his parents. May his example serve as an object lesson to all those who might be inclined to imitate him. In this way vice serves as its own tormentor.

Children are an extension of the lives of their fathers, and in painting a picture of the virtuous conduct of his eldest sons, we shall continue to speak of Edme R.

Edme-Nicolas is the second of Edme R.'s children. One can say of him what one reads in the lives of all canonised saints, he was virtuous from childhood. What is even more astonishing is that in his case a lively temperament was combined with a rare mind and with handsome features. His eagerness for study was unimaginable, and he damaged his health by devoting part of each night to it. His progress was as rapid as one might have expected, for if 'pertinax labor vincit naturam', unyielding labour aids nature more than it masters it. He taught philosophy for several years at the seminary in Auxerre, where they offered all subjects. And the most prominent townsfolk, almost all of whom were his pupils, still have a high regard for him. Then he became curate of Vermanton, one of the richest parishes in the diocese and close to his native village. He was greatly loved, even though he lived a retiring life, only appearing in public to perform his duties as a minister of the church.

After this curacy, he was appointed priest of Courgis, a small town close to Chablis. It was a large, poor parish, and the inhabitants were of a difficult disposition which they disguised beneath a pleasant manner. Moreover, they were exceedingly stubborn and deceitful.

Once he had acquired this benefice, Edme-Nicolas R. became so totally attached to it that he believed himself bound to his church by indissoluble ties. M. de Caylus was extremely fond of him. After ten years experience, the worthy prelate was delighted to observe that the conduct of this young man, for whom he had always had a special affection, accorded exactly with his expectations. And so he greeted the vicar of Courgis most warmly whenever he visited him in Régennes, and he singled him out one day in front of a huge gathering as the pride of his clergy. The prelate, knowing how wisely the young priest used the income from his benefice, wanted to give him a more important parish, to make him priest of Vermanton even, where he had been well-liked as a curate. He put the proposition to him through M. Creuzot, who was a respected priest in one of the parishes of the cathedral city, a truly apostolic man with such a pure and high sense of virtue that one can scarcely imagine anything loftier. But the young priest told M. Creuzot, who was his father-confessor, that he was wedded to the church at Courgis and would only give it up at his death. The reverend bishop was edified by his answer and, as every member of his flock was as dear to him as the others, he allowed Edme-Nicolas to remain where he wished. Indeed, what purpose would have been served in appointing him to a better living, since like a true shepherd he kept nothing for himself.

It is a consolation in our century that one finds here and there from time to time such worthy priests, who remind the rest of the clergy, by their example, of the proper use of wordly goods which are consecrated to God. In truth, they are usually to be found amongst parish priests, an order which is as worthy of respect as it is useful and poorly endowed with wordly goods. Edme-Nicolas R. never complained about the poverty of priests. On the contrary, I have often heard him express satisfaction that in this respect he and his fellow priests resembled Jesus. In his view, the moral rectitude of most of the priests of the lower order could be attributed to that blessed state of poverty, which Jesus made a law for his disciples, and which is a firm obligation for his ministers.

I shall present a totally truthful account of his behaviour, as I have already outlined it in *L'Ecole des Pères*, a work which has been justly acknowledged in Germany where it has been translated.

The priest of Courgis sees himself as the father of his parishioners, the arbiter of their differences, and the comforter and reliever of the sick. His one maxim in all his acts of charity is to give double what he has. This will become clearer in a moment. Though he has poor relatives, he gives them little, and he once justified his actions to one of them who had complained, in these terms: 'I am an important tithe-owner in the parish. My living brings me almost fifteen hundred livres a year, and five hundred francs are sufficient for the upkeep of my household. As for the rest, I wish it to remain in the parish which is so poor. However, I don't give my corn away. I let the poor and my own village have it at half-price in the winter, placing it on trust in their hands. I borrow from the rich to give to those who are less well-off, and when my half is returned to me in the summer months, I pay back what I have been loaned. And if I do not have sufficient, I go to the town to beg for charity, so as to spare the husbandmen from going. (That is how he gives more than he has). I adopted these poor people in accepting to be their parish priest. How could you expect my sermons to make the least impression on them, if I failed in my obligations and if I did not set an example of christian virtue? They know what I own and that whatever surplus I have belongs to them. I am for them the living image of Jesus Christ himself, and so I must feed them and win their affection if my teaching is to be acceptable to them, or I must give up my living. All I can do for you, my dear relation, is this; I have an income of approximately three hundred livres from my inheritance. Take some of that, since you have suffered misfortune this year, which God has brought upon you for your sanctification. Take half, for I have already disposed of the rest within the family. If it is not enough, I will reduce not my children's share but my own expenditure, in order to give it to you. I would joyfully eat nothing but bread to help my dear relations. But if you were in my position and were to visit these unfortunate people on their death-beds, whose only hope was in you and to whom you owed not only your worldly goods but your whole life, according to God's law, could you possibly neglect them and yet continue to believe in God, call yourself a christian, a minister, a priest?'

The relative had to agree that the priest of Courgis certainly did his duty.

This man has accepted to live a harder life than the least of his parishioners. All his time is usefully spent. He gets up at

three o'clock in the morning, and he meditates on the Holy
Scriptures until six for the instruction of his people. Then he
goes to the church to prepare for mass, which he celebrates at
seven o'clock. He usually remains on his knees before the altar
in the house of the Lord, awaiting those who need his
ministry, and a bell is rung to signal when it is time for him to
go to them to direct their consciences and give them fatherly
advice. Pastoral care such as this occupies him until midday,
unless there are sick people to be visited, and then he returns
home. He has lunch, after which he walks around his garden
for an hour in summer or in his study in winter. This room is
always fireless, even though he provides wood for all his
parishioners. During that hour he listens to all those who wish
to talk to him about their temporal needs, and in the afternoon
he does what he can to relieve their distress. Each week, he
visits people in the parish. Because of his gentleness and
kindness this happy day is eagerly awaited rather than feared,
as is said to be the case of another priest, who, though he
imitates his colleague in Courgis, does not temper his good
works, and whose expression always bears witness to the
severity of his moral code.

   He has founded schools at his own expense which are free.
The boys' school is looked after by Thomas R., who does not
consider such an important task beneath his dignity, the girls'
school by one of our sisters, and two widows of exemplary
conduct will take her place when she is gone. But the priest is
no less concerned with the welfare of the children. He obliges
parents to send them to school, in turn if their services are
needed; and as there are some who have to remain in the fields
all day long, the priest visits them in the evening, and once a
week he makes them read and write, providing them with
books and paper. The rest of the time, his brother Thomas R.
takes his place, as he in turn is replaced by the most prosperous and well-fed parishioners, whom the priest has enlisted to
devote one or two evenings a week to the education of these
unfortunate people. It seems that they are all the more
precious to their priest because their life is hard and because
they have difficulty in finding the means to educate themselves. If someone asks him: 'What use is education to these poor
people?', he replies: 'It gives them the most satisfying of

pleasures, that of knowing things and using their intelligence; a pleasure so considerable that, were one to suggest to a poor wretch that he could end his wretchedness by forgetting all he knew, he would rather renounce happiness. And that is why knowing God perfectly is a source of inexpressible bliss to the saints in heaven.' But this is not all he does, for he clothes them as well. The tithe on wine, which I have not yet referred to, is used for this purpose. It is in fact wrong to call this a tithe since it is only a twenty-first part, as it is for sheaves of corn. Out of twenty-one the priest takes just the last, which is much more reasonable as a tax and in the way it is applied than ours. This honest priest also encourages the poor to marry as he does the rich. He says that any man whose wealth is in the strength of his own two arms and who reaches the age of sixteen or seventeen sturdy and strong is a treasure to society, and one should make a man of him. Arts or crafts, give him whatever choice you like, he will undertake everything he does with the same enthusiasm, happy to earn his daily bread by his own labours. 'An active man creates a whirlwind around himself, like those which are said to exist around the planets', the good priest goes on. 'Ten at least of his fellow-men are stimulated by the activity of just one, and they make themselves useful. If I were to advise anyone to remain celibate', he adds, 'it would be the rich man, because he is born to be obeyed, and to have twenty, thirty, fifty men all working to look after him in his unproductive and ponderous existence. He creates another kind of whirlwind, much larger than the useful man's. He employs a thousand to feed, clothe and coddle no one but himself, whilst the active man alone feeds ten men and motivates them to feed another hundred. Don't imagine that the noble or the tax-collector who has castles built, his carriages painted and gilded, his clothes embroidered, who keeps prostitutes and an even baser retinue of flunkeys, don't imagine that he feeds all these people. He has lured them away from useful work. Elsewhere, they would have lived more frugally and contributed to the general good etc.'

In 1749, on October 22nd I believe, the worthy priest of Courgis suffered a cruel blow. One hundred and forty-nine houses in his parish were burnt to the ground. The bishop, M.

de Caylus, offered the poor people of his diocese a helping
hand, feeding them throughout the winter. And their incom-
parable priest went and sought help himself, and he also sent
circular letters to everyone in the surrounding district. No one
refused his request for help.

Amongst the priests who were visited, there was one who
lived between Tonnerre and Courgis and who was a true
philosophe. He lived from day to day, taking no heed for the
morrow, and he attributed such little importance to money
that he never locked it away. What he had was on the
mantlepiece over his old-fashioned fireplace, covered in ash
and soot. When a messenger from the burnt-out village called
on him and explained the reasons for his visit, the *philosophe*
priest sang the praises of the priest of Courgis, of his brother
Thomas who served as his curate, and of the good chaplain
M. Foynat, a fine man and a worthy priest. As all his
parishioners were well-to-do, the good priest took the messenger from door to door, urging his parishioners to give him
something. When they had returned to his house and he had
fed him at his own table, he said to him: 'Dear friend, you see
the mantlepiece, that's where I keep my money. Let us share
it.' He had a few louis and he insisted that the messenger
accept half. He also sent a friendly letter of greetings with his
gift to the three clergymen, whom he had in fact never met.

But after the bishop, the person who did most to help the
villagers who had lost their homes in the fire was M. Clément,
the treasurer of the cathedral and the brother and uncle of the
Cléments who were judges in the high-court in Paris. He had
an extremely high opinion of the priest of Courgis, which he
demonstrated on this occasion in the best possible way by
helping his parishioners.

But the parish priest did not stop at this. He journeyed to
Paris in search of even more financial assistance. He went with
recommendations from M. Clément and remained there
almost three months, secure in the knowledge that his flock
had not been abandoned to money-seekers. The worthy
chaplain, M. Foynat, celebrated mass, as Thomas R. was not
an ordained priest, but he took the catechism and read from
the scriptures in place of his elder brother's sermons. As a
result of all the financial help they received and the generous

loans made by M. Deschamps senior, who was a tax-collector
in Auxerre and Lord of the manor of Courgis, the village was
rebuilt and its inhabitants saved from beggary and vagrancy,
which would have destroyed their lives and been a loss to the
State.

The priest of Courgis had his enemies, but they never dared
draw too much attention to themselves as his conduct was
irreproachable, and he committed not the slightest indiscre-
tion. It is an infallible means of silencing calumny, and one
which young village priests could most usefully put into
practice.

Today, over sixty years old, the worthy priest seems more
zealous than ever, as he approaches the end of his labours and
prepares to receive his just reward. He has been held in as high
regard by M. de Caylus's successors as he was by M. de
Caylus himself. Of course, they knew him less well, but M.
de Caylus was like a second father to him and a good friend.

Yet, his parishioners hold one thing against him, that his
services and sermons are too long. There is some basis for this
complaint, and though the venerable priest's intention is to
curb in this way dangerous and frivolous pastimes and to
spend that one day which is set aside for the worship of God in
His service alone, he should perhaps have recognised that men
are not angels, and that some allowances must be made for
human frailty. His motives are, however, of the best, and one
is aware that as a servant of God, deeply conscious of his
obligations, he lives only to fulfil them properly.

May I, however, in respect of this last point, cite the wholly
different conduct of the venerable Pinard, an old priest in my
father's youth. Touslesjours speaks of him in *L'Ecole des Pères*.

'In Nitri, one used to see races in the meadow, as well as
wrestling and dancing. The good priest Pinard and Berthier,
the schoolmaster, did not denounce either these pastimes or
dancing on Sundays and feast-days, even though boys and
girls joined in together. Nothing indecent ever occurred.
Children who are used to seeing each other in school and at
catechism don't behave stupidly when they play together. It
would also be a good idea in those villages where it is
customary to shut girls up and keep them apart from boys, as
if one intended to make recluses of them. What happens in

these cases? It's like pulling the string on a cross-bow very taut. The tighter it is, the more violent the release. When young people like that have the chance to get together, it seems to me that they do wrong to take avantage of the situation. So our good priest would never hear of having separate schools, as some of the bourgeois from Noyers wanted who had settled in Nitri. And I might add that if our young people still show some restraint, they owe it to their communal schooling and to the fact that they see each other all the time. I know full well that one couldn't achieve the same results in town, but that's because the women and young girls are like pretty playthings that the men constantly want to touch. Their clothes and trinkets serve as bait. Men, and young boys even, can't look at them without feelings of desire. Nor does habit weaken it, since fashions change almost every day, giving them an entirely new appearance. With her coiffure alone, a townswoman can change her looks five or six times in a single day. Imagine then, what she can do with the rest of her finery, her rouge if she uses it, and all those baubles which she puts on to adorn herself. One of the villagers who has been a lackey in Paris told me all about it. Thus, a townsman marries twenty different women in one wife, whereas with us a girl is always the same, as her Sunday best isn't refined enough to change her completely. And so, I say again that there is no point in separating boys and girls when they are young. It would only give them ideas a few years later. We played different kinds of games. The men gathered in a large circle around us and watched. One wouldn't have dared do anything silly playing with the girls in front of these spectators. Far from disapproving of the men who spent their time watching these diversions, the priest encouraged them. "Go, go and watch the young ones running about," he would say. "Your presence will ensure that their fun is always innocent. I cannot be everywhere at once, and whenever I am absent every father must consider himself my deputy." In this way, the young people took some healthy excercise every Sunday, and the men enjoyed themselves. Joy shone on all their faces and everyone went home happy in the evening. Nowadays, such things no longer take place and the young people meet in secret and get up to all kinds of mischief.'

Father Pinard was not as devout as the parish priest of

Courgis, who is almost the only truly priestly figure in these parts. But he was an indulgent minister who always spoke sincerely, his eyes full of kindness, and who always had the welfare of his parishioners at heart. If you had seen the villagers gather round him after high mass on Sundays and feast-days, the way he greeted them and inquired about their families, you would have said: 'He's like a father with his children. Perhaps he is too kind, perhaps some wrongdoer will take advantage of his good nature, but upright hearts must surely value their religion and their obligations all the more highly.' Charles,* I remember his last years. Oh, how imposing was the air of godliness he wore on his calm, contented brow. What veneration his silvery locks inspired. The little worth I have in God's eyes I owe to that man and to his worthy helper. He permitted no legal disputes between us (his successors instituted them), always settling them himself, and perfectly able to tell right from wrong because he knew each one of us. His prayers in church and his sermons were short, but how he delivered them, and with what heartfelt words he preached! I remember a whole sermon he gave one Sunday in August. It had rained all night, but on Sunday it was fine and we asked if we could hold mass earlier, so that we could go and turn the swaths of corn and gather them into sheaves, ready for tying in the evening. He did not go up into the pulpit but simply came down to the chancel steps where he spoke to us: 'My children, God's children, I urge you to go and gather up your sheaves on this fine morning. The law which governs you is a benevolent law, for you live under the gentle yoke of God's heavenly goodness. Give thanks to Him. Those who were bound by the law of Moses would not have been allowed to violate the sabbath in this manner. But we, children of the redemption, are freed from the letter of the law which kills, and from its subjugation. The single obligation which God imposes on us, a duty which repays a hundred-fold, is that we should love him and our fellow-men. By loving God we achieve peace and satisfaction in this life. In loving our fellow-men we are loved in return. We give and we receive. Oh my children, let us love each other. I ask those

* Young Roger's preceptor in *L'Ecole des Pères* who takes him to Saci and Nitri to further his education.

who have no crops to harvest to help those who have. Their
labour will be of greater value than attending mass. My
children, the bell for vespers will be rung, but do not come
today. Be with me in prayerful thought, and I will say them in
the name of my children, kneeling at the foot of the sacred
font where I received your promises of faithfulness to God.
Our good schoolmaster, your second father, and a few old
men will join me. My children, may God confirm the blessing
which I give you in his name.' The lessons he gave us young
people were always suited to our understanding, practical in
tone and sensible, which made what he said convincing. When
he dealt with a moral point, he asked all of us our views as to
what advantage it might bring to men. He explained it so
clearly, that even the most dull-witted could express an
opinion. Then he would repeat what everyone had said,
correcting and developing it, and emphasising above all the
importance of living a good life.'

He is, I believe, the embodiment of the true country priest.
But not everyone sees things in the same light, and,
moreover, I would not presume to give advice to my worthy
eldest brother. He is more intelligent, more learned, more
experienced than I, and I am sure that the path he has chosen is
the one which truly suits his parishioners' cast of mind. The
same remedy is not suitable for all the sick.

Thomas R., who is several years younger than his brother,
has that same happy disposition as those who are depicted
living in the golden age. His openness and honesty show in his
face, and as soon as he speaks one feels that one can trust him.
This worthy cleric is so modest that he would never accept the
ordination which M. de Caylus offered him on several
occasions. The bishop even went so far as to write to him:

'I know what holds you back. Because you are inferior to
your elder brother, you believe yourself unfit. But, my dear
son, there aren't three individuals in my whole diocese like
your brother, not even two perhaps. You mustn't compare
yourself with him. One can be his inferior by far, and still
most worthy. I ask you to yield; if you do not, I tell you as
your bishop that you must answer to God for the use to which
you have put this gift of saving souls with which he has
endowed you.'

These words alarmed Thomas R., but the village priest was
happy to keep him, and he went to Régennes to speak on his
behalf. He pointed out how useful his brother was to him as a
teacher in such a large parish, and so on.

'But he has no secure living.'

'He does not wish for one. God is the father of all men.'

Such a disinterested reply was applauded by the bishop,
who, in return, sent his pastoral blessing to a cleric 'who
preferred to be last in God's house rather than first in the
palaces of the wicked.'

To say more about Thomas R. would detract from the
simplicity of the subject. Furthermore, my fear that this work
might fall into the hands of my esteemed brothers prevents me
from writing as much as I would like. Having satisfied myself
with a few words of praise, I shall give them pleasure by
saying no more.

Barbe Ferlet survived her husband by five years. She died in
July 1772. We behaved towards her exactly as my venerable
father had behaved towards his own mother. With our full
consent, she managed our inheritance, which was hers to
dispose of until the day she died.

THE PLOUGHMAN'S WIFE

This I can truly say, is the story of the model wife; one who fulfilled all her obligations to her country, her husband, her children, her servants, in a word towards everyone connected with her.

Barbare Ferlet, a young fair-haired girl with the most charming face, had an elder sister called Elisabeth, who was seemingly as good and as quiet as Barbare was lively, malicious, and even a little naughty. The two sisters were sixteen and twenty-two respectively when a fire ruined their father, a respectable man, who lost some antique furniture and several title deeds, which bore witness to the family's former comfortable circumstances. Elisabeth, who before the event had been courted by an eligible suitor, was forsaken by him, but she got over it. She respected Claude Mairat, a poor day-labourer who worked on the river, who had previously not dared to aspire to her hand. Seeing her impoverished, he took it upon himself to come and speak to the good Nicolas Ferlet in the following manner.

'Sir (for your poverty will never prevent me from addressing you thus), you are now ruined. M. Charuat, who sought your daughter Babet's hand, has withdrawn. And I thought that what you needed in your situation, a widower of advanced years, was a working son-in-law rather than a gentleman. So I have come to offer myself as your obedient son and son-in-law. For I've been fond of your daughter as long as I can remember. I beg you therefore to give her to me so that I may serve you, as is my inclination, and make her happy by showing her greater affection than any boy ever had for any girl. And this will rebound on her kind father, the most honest and the worthiest man in the parish, and perhaps in the whole world. And I promise to be a good brother to Mlle Barbare, your younger daughter, whom I will oblige and serve better than if we had been born of the same womb.'

Old Ferlet, hearing the good lad speak in this manner, whose face was more expressive than his words, was touched and answered him thus:

'Claude, my boy, your request is of some importance and such matters cannot be settled in a day. So let me reflect upon them. But I want you to know that what you said pleased me because it revealed your kind heart.'

Nicolas Ferlet questioned his elder daughter, who modestly gave her father to understand that Mairat was the very man they needed. They spoke in front of Barbare, and she said that she wouldn't want a river man, but if a good ploughman came along she would rather have him, whatever sorrow this might bring thereafter. Her father, who loved her with a special affection (for beauty always was the first goddess idolized by mortals), praised her sentiments and spoke highly of ploughing. However, he gave Babet to the good Mairat, who kept his word and by his labour relieved the old man's poverty.

Some time after this happy marriage in which the partners were rich only in virtue, Charuat, whose surname was La Ramée, courted Barbare. Old Ferlet was delighted. 'He's an excellent match, my girl,' he said to his younger daughter. 'When he withdrew he showed disdain for us, but by returning he treats us once more as he did at first. Moreover, he's rich. He is the general agent of the wood-merchants and may one day become a contractor. He is sensible, hard-working, and sober.' 'I am your daughter,' replied Barbare, 'and I must submit to your will. However, will you permit me to talk to you as if I were your sister?' 'As if you were my sister? of course my girl; and what's more, you are my friend. Speak my child.'

'I'll tell you then, with all the respect that I owe you father, that La Ramée is of all the marriageable men the last one I would take. What! He abandoned my sister, a faultless girl and the living proof of this as a wife, just because you and she needed him a little more than before. You want me to take him? You can see that what attracts him to me is that I'm quite pretty. That man is giving way in spite of himself to a passion which dominates him. But I should be unhappy as his wife, once he had had his pleasures with me. All he would be left with is his injured self-esteem. And he would look upon you with disdain. You'd see, my poor dear father, how he'd look at you. Therefore, if you consent, I think I shall refuse him as he refused my sister the last time you spoke to him. And I shall wait until a good and blameless husband is found for me, and a good son-in-law for you like my brother-in-law, and I shall go on serving you and helping my sister with the housework.' There were tears in old Ferlet's eyes as he listened to his daughter who was then just eighteen years old. 'Oh how wrongly named you are,' he said to her, 'and what good sense you have for your age. One would have thought that you had received the same education as our noble ancestors. But we mustn't turn La Ramée down with a show of disdain. On the contrary, I will tell him that you don't wish to marry. That will be best.' 'As you please, father, and how kind you are to yield to my wishes.' 'It's because reason dictates it also, and I respect reason in my daughter as I respected it in the virtuous Barbare Alliot, your worthy mother.'

La Ramée did not fail to return to renew his proposition. But old Ferlet replied as they had agreed; and the fellow, who was as proud as he was selfish, revealed his unpleasant character in his response. Afterwards, the old man said to Barbare 'You were right, my girl, and I realise how wise and prudent you are.' The refusal was no less pleasing to Babet, for, although in her kindness she was as concerned for her younger sister's well-being as she was for her own, she was piqued by Charuat and she enjoyed seeing him treated as he had treated her. And lastly, one wouldn't have expected Mairat to like the man who might have deprived him of his sweetheart and of the wife who made him so happy had it not been for the fire which ruined the good Ferlet. He too congratulated Barbare and promised that he would find a husband worthy of her, even if he had to travel to the ends of the earth. He didn't go that far.

Five miles from Accolai, the place where these good people dwelt, there lived a man who resembled the patriarchs described in the Bible, and a man worthy of his title. He cultivated the land, but was endowed with talents which exceeded those of ordinary peasants. This worthy fellow added to his skills as a ploughman those other country crafts, which are the foremost of the arts and the noblest means whereby a man may create wealth. This ploughman had been left a widower at thirty-four with a large family to look after. He had seven children from his first marriage. He learned from Mairat of Barbare's reply to La Ramée's request, and he was amazed, as everyone else in the district was, by such nobility in a young girl, and whom everyone had considered a scatter-brain until then. He had never met her. One day, when he was on business at the fair at Vermanton, a large town near Accolai, Edme Rameau (for that was the widower's name) heard people talking about Barbare and about her refusal. One man said he'd just seen her with her father and sister and named the inn where they were. Edme Rameau went there to greet the father whom he knew and to see the daughter for whom his heart already showed some interest, though she was unknown to him. He found father, daughter, Mairat and his wife as they were about to start a frugal lunch. Old Ferlet admired Edme Rameau. He greeted him first warmheartedly. 'Here is the most upright man in the neighbourhood,' he said to his children. 'Good day, M. Rameau.'

'Your humble servant, M. Ferlet. And this is your dear family?'

'Yes this is my son-in-law, my elder daughter, my younger daughter.'

'The wrongly named Mlle Barbare,' Edme Rameau said.

'Yes sir, the wrongly named, but it is her mother's name and she was also wrongly named, for mother and daughter have always been good and gentle creatures. The one made me a very happy husband and very happy father, the other relieves my widowhood and my old age. Never were there better daughters than mine.'

'Agreed,' cried his son-in-law, 'for I was beginning to be jealous of my little sister. And, let it be said without displeasing you, my wife is certainly her equal.'

'Ah, son-in-law', cried old Ferlet, a tear in his eye, 'such praise for your wife pleases me coming from your lips.'

Mairat began to laugh as he looked at Barbare. 'You're not cross with me, dear little sister?'

'For speaking well of my dear kind sister! Oh Mairat! you couldn't express all that I think of her.'

'What a happy family!' said Edme Rameau. 'Permit me, sir, to have my dinner served with yours.'

'It's an honour, M. Rameau.'

'There will be plenty for me . . . I've brought cutlets of fresh pork, eggs, butter and bread. They will only have to provide us with wine.' He had the cutlets put in the pan, and they were cooked in no time. A generous omelette accompanied them. He took from his bag an excellent home-made loaf, a few dried fruits, some walnuts, some grapes which had been put in the oven, some hazelnuts, and the table was furnished. Old Ferlet and his family had brought a gudgeon caught by Mairat (for he had an understanding with the ploughman). It was a treat for Rameau who lived far from the river. Everyone was contented and could choose what he or she liked most. Vermanton wine is one of the best in lower Burgundy and is sold in large quantities. The men drank in moderation yet with that great thirst which the keen air of a dry and mountainous region gives one. All three of them loved the wine, but all three of them feared equally over-indulgence.

When the wine had mellowed the old man's spirit, producing that pleasant sense of contentment which precedes drunkenness, Edme Rameau, who was beginning to appreciate Barbare more and more, said with a smile, 'Before I saw this charming person, I had a plan, but the more I look at her the more I feel I shall have to change it.'

'Oh! what is this plan,' asked Mairat.

'Mlle Barbare is too good-looking . . . and with the family that she comes from, for I know your origins M. Ferlet. Your family, like mine, has not been dishonoured, for an honest man is still honourable even if impoverished, reduced to working.'

Hearing this word, the old man stood up, beside himself with emotion, 'You remind me of my former nobility,' he said. 'It is a fond and dear memory. But work is the ultimate succour of honour and nobility. You work, don't you my dear Rameau?'

'Yes, and like our first father, cultivating the land with the sweat of my brow. But I thank God for it, for it is the foremost of the arts. I am a ploughman as you know.'

Barbare blushed and looked quite lovely. Her sister, who noticed this, kissed her, trying to hide her blushes from the men, and said in her ear:

'He's just the one for you, the most upright man in the district, but he's too rich for us.'

'Didn't I hear you say something to me about Barbare, M. Rameau?' old Ferlet remarked.

'I said, or meant to say, that your younger daughter is destined to raise your family up, for if a prince saw her he would become her obedient servant. As for myself, I had heard so many good things spoken of her that I desired to meet her. And I had even come to Vermanton today with the intention of going on to your village in order to see her, when I learned that she was here with her worthy father, her greatly esteemed sister, of whom any husband of Barbare's will be proud, and with your honest son-in-law whom I respect like everyone else.'

'You fill my last days with joy,' old Ferlet replied, 'saying such kind things about me and my family. May God bless you for them, as I do, M. Rameau. But what did you wish to say about Barbare?'

'That I am unworthy of her.'

'A gentleman not worthy of my daughter? A descendant of the most upright people in the district, whose ancestors were noble like mine? Who, then will be?'

'I am a widower, I have seven children, and I would do Mlle Barbare wrong; for she may find a rich suitor, a nobleman even, with her beauty. But I only know what thoughts were already in my mind. It was her true worth and the prudent reply she made to La Ramée's request which won my admiration and caused me rashly to desire her even before I had met her.'

'Rashly!' cried old Ferlet. 'It is for Barbare to tell us if she thinks it was rash.'

But the young girl instead of answering her father's question blushed so violently and appeared to be so embarrassed, that he didn't dare press her further. The reason was that Edme Rameau, as well as having great personal qualities and a reputation for uprightness the equal of his renown as a ploughman, was the most handsome man in the district.

'I see,' the honest man replied, 'that Mlle Barbare thinks as I do. I shall therefore remove these thoughts from my mind.'

'If you think you read something in my thoughts which does not do you honour,' Barbare replied modestly, 'you are wrong.'

These few words filled the ploughman's heart with joy, and old Ferlet exclaimed, 'That's the answer I would have expected from my child.'

'If I dared to think that my quest would not be disagreeable to the fair Barbare, I would not desist.'

'No, no,' replied old Ferlet.'

'No,' said Mairat, shaking Rameau's hand.

'No, M. Edmond,' said Babet, 'no, I can answer for that.'

As for Barbare, she was as red as a full moon when it rises above the horizon between two tiny clouds which veil its appearance.

'In that case,' answered Edme Rameau, 'seeing that I am accepted by the whole family, I ask M. Ferlet's permission to visit him, this not being a suitable place in my eyes for such a dignified and serious matter.'

Then they turned their attention to eating and making merry, at the same time exchanging many pleasantries. When the meal was over, Edme Rameau led the Ferlet family back to the boat which travelled the river Cure. There they fixed the following Sunday for Edme to make his proposal. It was Thursday, and so there were only three days to wait.

Barbare was thoughtful and day-dreamed on the way home. Her father asked her, 'Does Edme Rameau's honourable proposal cause you heartache my child?'

'No, father, but the difference between a daughter and a wife is so great that I wonder at it. What is more, it is so serious a step and of such importance that one can't think too much about it.'

'But does the request itself displease you?'

'No, father. I remember you telling me that you are descended from noblemen. And the first estate after the nobility is that of the ploughman. He will bring me closer again to our former condition.'

'Good girl, your answer is sound and true. May God bless you, for you have noble sentiments.'

Alone with her elder sister, Barbare explained herself more freely. When her sister asked her if she was attracted to Edme Rameau, she replied:

'I find him such a fine man that I consider this chance as a reward for my tender feelings for my father. I shall certainly love him, even though he is a widower with seven children; and I shall treat them well and they will love me in return. I do not wish to behave as a step-mother to them, but like a sister to the grown-up girls and as a mother to the little ones. As for the boys, I shall maintain an attitude of reserve, only intervening to reconcile them with their father if they happen to anger him. As for my other duties, I shall hope to fulfil them all; working, looking after the home without meanness and without wastefulness, though I shall be in a rich household. And I shall try not to bring shame upon my husband with the former nor to cause him concern with the latter. To achieve this, I shall study your example, sister, with more attention than ever. For when your mother is no longer there, your elder sister replaces her and you must imitate and respect her like the one whose place she takes.' Babet was moved to tears at the memory of her dear mother, and looking at Barbare she said:

'If I replace our dear mother by my seniority, you take her place in name and appearance, and I respect you as I did that worthy wife and mother.'

'I owe you the same respect as the living image of my dear father.' Barbare replied, kissing her and mingling her own tears with those of her sister.

At that moment Mairat and their father came in. 'What devoted sisters,' the old man said to his son-in-law. 'But you are crying.'

'Yes father,' replied Babet, 'it's the memory of my dear and worthy mother, of whom Barbare bears the name and is the living image. That's what I was telling her.'

Hearing these words which renewed his grief, the old man stood motionless and his tears flowed.

'Oh, unhappy girl that I am,' cried Babet, 'for I make my father weep!'

'And may you be blessed my dear daughter, for causing a husband such tender sorrow at the loss of the best of wives and mothers, one who was so dear to me. For it is her resemblance and her name that I find in your sister Barbare which makes her even more dear to me. In my love for you, my elder daughter, it is myself I love, but in your sister it is your poor mother, and that is why she was the one I always cuddled more.'

'Oh father,' replied Babet, 'how you endear my sister to me and how you increase the sorrow I shall feel at being separated from her so soon as a result of her happy marriage. For she is well disposed to Edme Rameau. She has revealed her kind heart to me and has shown her fine feelings as a future wife and step-mother.'

'May God be praised, my girls, and for Edme Rameau, who although a widower is nonetheless the best match in the whole district; seeing that he owns the finest farm in the region, even better than Courtenai which belonged to his great-grand-father's family. Moreover, his is a good family and well connected to noblemen and presiding judges.'

'What you tell me, father, gives me great pleasure, remarked Barbare, for I am a little haughty and proud. I see that the good Lord shows his tolerance, since he sends me a husband whose character and family will make easier the obedience which a wife owes her husband, as the Church does to Jesus, of which I have read in my prayer-book in the epistle on marriage.'

On Sunday morning, just before high mass, whilst Barbare was still at her toilet and old Ferlet and Mairat were looking after the breakfast prepared by Babet, Edme Rameau arrived on a fine horse called Flamand, a good and faithful animal which almost seemed to be endowed with powers of reason. The master and his horse were greeted warmly by the old man, who had the highest opinion of the one as well as a passionate love of horses. Old Ferlet no longer had a stable since his ruinous fire, but seeing the beauty, gentleness, and temperament of the animal led him into the house and placed him beside the bed, which served as a stable-rack.

'Mairat, give the master something to drink,' the good old man said to his son-in-law, 'whilst I take care of his travelling companion. "He who loves the horse loves the master" is as true a proverb as when it is applied to a dog.' And he gave some mixed oats to Flamand who seemed to look at his master with satisfaction. Then the old man called his two daughters and sat down at the table.

'How are you, my friend?' he asked Edme R.

'You are most kind and polite, worthy and venerable sir,' and taking Mairat's hand he went on, 'see how this worthy man can read into people's hearts. He knows how much I value this fine animal, my old servant who adorns my plough and who is the best-natured mount in the whole world. He takes care of him first of all, knowing full well that at home when he returns from his labours Flamand and his friends are given refreshment before their master. But here is Mlle Barbare. Will you permit me, dearest father, to greet her as my future wife?'

'Yes, my friend, greet her as such.'

And Edme Rameau kissed her on both cheeks and said to her:

'With your father's permission, I greet you as my future companion and my partner in all that God has in store for me, whether pleasure or pain. May you be blessed dear girl, since you do not despise a man who is already a father and widower and therefore has a greater need of a helper because of all his labours, but who would never have thought of taking one had he learnt that you were already married. There, I have made my proposal M. Ferlet, Mairat my friend, my dear sister Mme Mairat.'

'And it has been accepted by me, my daughter, my son-in-law and his wife,' replied old Ferlet. Then he poured himself and each of his children a full cup, saying: 'Let us drink to our happy couple.' 'To our happy couple,' they all repeated. They had a quick breakfast, for the third bell for high mass (which is always rung on the priest's command as he gives the signal) was about to be rung, and old Ferlet did not wish to disgrace himself by arriving last at church. Edme Rameau accompanied Barbare, which is the sign of a marriage, and placed himself beside her in the women's pew, whilst Mairat and the old man took their usual places in the choir. Barbare's devotion was a new source of delight to her future husband. And the priest, who knew Edme Rameau, looked towards the Ferlet pew when he went into the pulpit to give his sermon. He saw a man whom he admired next to Barbare. The venerable minister of God was overjoyed, as he was connected with the Ferlet family, and was delighted that its fortunes would be a little restored. He gave a short talk in which he expressed his satisfaction at the happiness of one of his flock, whose true worth, beauty even, he exalted, as well as her double devotion as a daughter and to God. When the service was over they returned to the house. Edme Rameau drew up the details of the marriage contract, which were very advantageous to his future wife without doing harm to the children of his first marriage. Then they had lunch at which Barbare served most graciously. When the meal was over they took their banns to the priest: 'I congratulate you, M. Rameau, for having chosen so well,' this worthy man said to the future husband. 'For Barbare is of even greater merit than her honest father thinks, and he thinks most highly of her. But I have studied her. You will have a treasure. At first let her follow her own inclinations, and then come and sing her praises to me in due course.' These remarks made a favourable impression on the prospective husband. They were true, and there was never any cause to detract from what had been said.

The marriage took place three weeks later. Edme Rameau had brought all his children, and he returned home the same evening with his new wife.

The next day, Barbare, who from now on was to be Mme Rameau, rose from her bed a wife, a mother, and the governess of a household in which every day there were twenty-two people, that is to say her husband, herself and the children, and thirteen male and female servants. She said a short prayer as she got up, then, lively as she was, she set to work without undue haste but with equal adroitness and grace. Her husband pretended not to notice anything and left her to do as she wished. Only the eldest daughter helped her stepmother, showing her where everything was kept. Barbare was a good village cook, for she had learnt this skill from her mother and sister. The breakfast-cum-lunch for the servants was excellent. Her husband wanted to taste it, but without being seen. He was surprised by it and thought the expenditure of the household was bound to double. However he said nothing. He simply kept an eye on the salting-tubs for the pork, the reserve supplies of eggs, the dried fruit, the rape-wine, for the peasants had to have a wine which rasped their throat so that they felt it going down, the dried cheeses, in a word all the provisions one would have in the country. Once the servants' meal was over and they had all gone back to their jobs, Barbare went to hear mass with her step-daughters who were five in number. She left home as the bell rang and did not remain a moment after the words 'Ite missa est'*. She returned in haste and busied herself in the house, ensuring that everything was neat and tidy. Then she began to think about the family dinner. For the first few days they feasted themselves. There was game, poultry, and other extraordinary dishes. The priest, the schoolmaster, and other distinguished people were invited. Everything was ready when they arrived, and a delicious aroma filled their nostrils and promised that their appetite would be satisfied. The guests couldn't stop praising the dishes. Her husband was delighted, but inwardly he thought to himself: 'We shan't always dine so well. My wife seems amenable and I shall encourage her to be thrifty. I'm delighted, however, that she knows how to cook. There are many occasions on which it gives much pleasure.'

Once the days of entertaining guests had passed, Barbare didn't have so much to do. A single good dish made up the whole meal. Noticing the simpler fare, her husband said to his wife: 'Our ordinary meals are very good, and better than I have ever had. Do you think our provisions are adequate? Each year I kill four pigs weighing a little over a hundred-weight, ten of my oldest sheep at wine-harvest time and in the winter. We were consuming five pounds of beef or cow a week. I have between one hundred and fifty and two hundred hens, and I was selling twelve dozen eggs a week in summer, with some left over for the household. That enabled me to buy salt, spices, and all the other provisions one needs in a house. My twenty-four cows brought me nine francs each market day, that's to say eighteen francs a week, not counting what we use for our own daily consumption. My walnut trees provide me with oil for salads all the year round, nuts for everyone at tea-time and for dessert in winter. And I still used

---

* Go now, the mass is over.

to sell one hundred crowns' worth each year. I shan't even mention my wheat and my wine. Everyone here eats and drinks his fill, and I'm the wheat and wine merchant.'

'In a month's time I will show you what my accounts will be, husband. I would have shown you them earlier but for the expense of our hospitality.'

'Agreed, my dear wife.'

One month later and six weeks after their marriage, the young wife showed her accounts to her husband. But it must be said that she had come in the best months for the garden, the hens, and the milk. Edme Rameau looked at them in puzzlement. He noticed that there was an increase of a third in the receipts of the produce of the farm-yard and a third saved on the expenditure. He thought he must be mistaken and did the calculations several times. Finally, he asked how it had been achieved and begged his wife to see if she hadn't forgotten anything. She assured him they were correct, and he was convinced. Then she said to him: 'You mustn't be cross with your eldest daughters, husband, because they were less economical than I. It is not that they are without merit. They have a great deal. Nannette and Marie will be good wives one day, but when two or three are running things, one wants this, the other wants that, and these differences of opinion lead to greater expense. The work itself is not so well done because each expects things of the other. Your linen was in a bad state, and I am putting it in order together with all the rest because I consider myself to be in charge of everything. If I receive help, so much the better, but I don't expect it. At home I left my sister Babet to look after things, and I only busied myself with my own sewing. But because she loved me dearly, she made me run the house on my own for a week from time to time and kept an eye on me. And that is how I learned to do it, not with her, but alone, knowing that I had sole charge of everything. The food had to be good and frugal because my father wasn't rich, and he had been used to my dear mother's way of preparing it which was both excellent and economical. That is why my sister strove to do as her mother had done, and she set me a good example especially most recently. I try to do a lot with a little like my mother and sister, but notice that most of what I save results from what I get from the garden. It was almost wild and contained only useless plants. Now it abounds in spinach, cabbages, lettuces, chervil, purslane and beet. I even use the tender leaves of the turnips. I make generous omelettes for your servants, which they find excellent, as well as for us, yet I only use half the eggs your daughters tell me to. These economies enable me to give you and your servants a little dish of spinach or an extra salad. Your daughters tell me that in the past you used only to eat two or three salads a year. Now you have one every day. And I gather that your servants, who love vinegar, are delighted. You also save a great deal of oil because of the natural taste peasants have for vinegar. I make it myself from the stale, light-red wine which remains on the lees, which I mix with a little rape-wine each week. Salad makes a change and stimulates the appetite. Your ploughboys leave the table refreshed and satisfied. Your garden is huge, husband. I've asked the ploughboys to work there with us when they return from the fields. They dig, and your children and I do the rest. It's a recreation. I'm going to fill it with gooseberry bushes, strawberry plants, raspberries in the parts shaded by the wall where nothing else grows, cherry, plum and apple trees. There won't be a corner which isn't cultivated, and it alone will earn you more than twenty acres of wheat. My father's garden was only as big as one of your small plots, and it provided us with cheap produce during our years of poverty. Spinach yields an astonishing amount. The sorrel will ornament the borders instead of thyme and useless bushes. The gooseberries will be spaced out, with the dwarf apple trees between them. Even your farm-yard will be planted, leaving a track for the carts. You are young, so plant walnut trees on both sides of the driveway to your farm. But that is your concern, and I shall only occupy myself with the garden. Not a vegetable will be lacking, and I shall often regale your servants with them to encourage them to work there. If you tell me which vegetables you prefer, you can be sure that there will always be an abundance of them. I shall double the number of your hens with the eggs I am hatching this year. I have a talent for raising chicks and you will lose very few of them. Your sheep will double also, as I know how to rear lambs. We only had a few sheep as we didn't have much room, but they were very useful. Here you have room and grazing. A shepherd can as easily look after three hundred as one hundred and fifty. Look at that pond. At your discretion I will have a fence put up which will divide it in two. The lower part I can use to raise geese and ducks. Besides providing food, I shall get feather beds from them, and I hope to provide each of your children whom you marry off with a fine trousseau. All this will cost you nothing as you live in an isolated spot. They can all be fed from your barn with what is scattered when the wheat is threshed and winnowed. Your enclosed meadow over there will give you enough grazing, up to six months after you have cut the hay, for twice the number of cows you have at present. In winter you will have sufficient straw. These animals will increase your manure. You have a dove-cot in which you keep bundles of vine twigs. Let us keep feather-legged pigeons in it, as they don't inconvenience the countryman. They will feed on the vetch which you sow on your fallow land and which you graze the horses on. I tell you, that with all that you have, your daily expenditure will no longer be taken out of your earnings from the land. I have nothing to say about the pigs. Your practice of keeping a farrowing sow is such an excellent one that you sell piglets instead of buying them. It is rare to have such a good sow as yours which regularly produces twelve piglets each litter. But she had been badly neglected before our marriage and was so thin and exhausted that she only produced runts. But look at the most recent ones, they promise to be very sturdy. All will be well then, husband, and the more so since looking after everything is for me an enjoyable occupation, and a pleasure rather than an occupation.'

Edme Rameau was delighted with all these observations, which were not made on a single occasion, but which had to be set down together here. This honest ploughman experi-enced the calmest contentment a sensible husband could enjoy, that of having full confidence in his wife's ability to run the household, leaving him free to busy himself with the affairs of the farm. He made money, as is a man's duty, provided for the family, and could be certain that he was placing the fruits of his labour in good hands. For the money was saved and kept by Barbare, as is the duty of a wife.

As a housekeeper, the pretty ploughman's wife was a model: active, sensible, hard-working. She liked only activities which were profitable, and even her pastimes were productive. But it is not in this respect that she is most to be admired and considered worthy of being offered as a model to all her sex. It is rather as a wife, mother, and step-mother.

As a wife, Barbare had all the qualities, all the proper sentiments. She looked upon her husband as her guide, her lord, her master, and her father. Her attitude was a far cry from the dangerous and criminal system of equality which is advocated only by libertines in towns. She believed herself to be dependent and was submissive, not as a slave but as a daughter. Never did a women love her husband so much. All her affection, all her desires were devoted to him, and she looked upon him as the only man in the world. Two fundamental concerns determined her behaviour towards her dear husband, her charm and her conversation. The latter occupied her no more than the former. The ploughman's labours were extremely arduous and unceasing. And so the care which Barbare took of him was part of her daily tasks, which she regulated according to the nature of the work, the season, and her husband's state of health. This was the task she cherished most, her favourite occupation, the one which gave her the greatest pleasure. Even being in her husband's arms did not give her more pleasure than concerning herself with his comfort, preventing any ailments, or relieving them. When he arrived home, Edme Rameau was a king, a god whom everyone rushed to serve, and who was welcomed with the most zealous attention, in a cool spot in summer, in winter beside the fire. He was offered warmed slippers, a fur-lined cap, a comfortable chair, a large glass of hot wine, before being greeted with a kiss. And even as she heard him approaching a long way off, Barbare would exclaim: 'Your father is coming, children; quickly, quickly, move yourselves from his place.' And this dearly loved husband and father would be left in peace to warm himself. Meanwhile, they finished preparing the supper. The table was brought up to him, and they waited until he had turned around before beginning. It wasn't like it is here, 'Madame is served.' There Madame served her hard-working master. She waited fondly, respectfully until he was

ready to eat. Then she placed herself next to him, in the
second chair, served him whatever he would enjoy, and took
an inexpressible delight in seeing him contented; overjoyed by
the warm and tender attention which was shown him. When
he and the rest of the family had eaten, the table was cleared.
His wife kept an eye on what might be served again, and she
also watched over the feeding of the animals, those useful
companions of their masters. Once that was done, she returned to her place beside her husband. The rest of the family,
however, children and servants alike, had formed a circle
around the huge, old-fashioned fireplace. Two bundles of
vine twigs, a large faggot from the branch of an oak tree, and
a few lumps of coal were thrown onto it. Together, they
produced a bright and blazing fire so that everyone drew back
and each was equally warmed. Whilst the whole family took
pleasure in this, particularly in winter and especially the
peasants who wore only light cloth, the head of the household
played the leading part. He talked, told stories, gave instruc-
tions. He was listened to with rapt attention, his wife setting
an example. Edme Rameau had a sense of humour. He had
visited Paris where he had been a magistrate's clerk, and he
knew a thousand and one stories of interest to children and
poor peasants who had never left their village. Barbare too
had read, and her husband often asked her to speak. This she
did with grace and modesty, saying only things that set a
good example, whether acquired from her reading, from her
late mother, or from her good sister. In this, she imitated her
husband who often recounted the good examples he had
learnt from his respectable father and virtuous mother. He
told how he respected them whilst they lived and regretted
them after their death, and how he had been a father to his two
sisters, etc. These winter evenings, whatever the subject of the
conversation, always ended with the reading of a chapter from
the Gallic Bible, which was handed down in the Rameau
family. In Advent, the head of the household sang carols
which the family repeated in chorus. What is remarkable is
that they were contained in a large volume in octavo printed
in Paris, and the carols were much more meaningful than those
in the great sacred book of carols. After the reading of a
chapter from the Bible, the head of the household knelt down

and recited the Lord's prayer and the Creed in French, a short prayer requesting a quiet night, and the Nunc Dimittis. He then bade everyone goodnight and went to his bed, which his wife had warmed during his prayer, kneeling down beside their place of rest. During all the winter evenings, except when carols were sung, the lads prepared stakes for the vines whilst they talked, and the girls stripped flax or spun. Their mother set an example. This part of the evening was given up to going over all her husband's things to see which needed attention. And she would do mending as she listened.

In the summer when her husband was busy with the hard toil of hay-making and harvesting the grain, Barbare prepared refreshments for him and a change of clothing if he was sweating. At the first sound of the horses returning home, as she knew that her husband would take more care of these animals than of himself, she would rush out to him with a large silver goblet full of wine and make him drink it before tending the animals. 'Drink quickly, husband, as you are hot. A man like you is very precious and taking care of you must be our first consideration.' Then she would watch over him attentively, seeing that he didn't catch a chill She would go back out to him if he didn't come in quickly enough and would wipe the sweat from his brow and from his back. She made him put on a shirt and a jacket. And when he was settled, she gave him refreshing things which he liked. For, after a few years of marriage, she had succeeded in having enough to satisfy any taste for dairy produce and for fruits such as strawberries, raspberries, gooseberries, melons, pears, apricots, blackberries, apples, chestnuts, fine grapes, and fruits to cook. Being a good country pastrycook, she was also in the habit of giving her household, and above all her husband and family, pastries as a treat on the two days of the week when she baked bread. She made spinach pasties which were so delicious that no-one ever tired of them. She also made leek pasties for the servants because coarse peasants like strong things. She made very thin flat-cakes with butter and raised dough whilst the oven was heating up, and she sent the servants out with them, piping hot, to the men who were working. It was a feast they enjoyed so much that when day labourers could not be found for work on the vines, they flocked to Edme Rameau's to be feasted. Thus this worthy wife and mother brought her husband benefit and happiness as a result of her behaviour and understanding in all things.

As a mother Barbare Ferlet, wife of Rameau, was so deserving of praise and so exemplary that one might consider her a paragon. She had a son in the first year of her marriage who was called Nicolas-Edme. His elder brother Edme-Nicolas acted as his godfather in the name of old Nicolas Ferlet, and his eldest sister Nanette Rameau was his godmother. He was a child of rare beauty and was admired by everyone. But he did not have such a happy disposition. He was stubborn, petulant, and resourceful only in destructive ways. He took everything he could from home to give to his little friends. Because of the children of the first marriage, Barbare corrected him with a certain severity, often to the extent that they intervened on behalf of the guilty little lad, who repaid them with ingratitude. But he was such a sweet child that they all had a soft spot for him and adored him and let him get away with things even when they quarrelled with his mother. It touched Barbare to the quick to have a child with such a character. One day she wept and poured all her woes out to her worthy father, old Ferlet, who had come to see her. 'Daughter, I am going to watch your son during the two days holiday I am to spend with you,' the honest man said, 'and, before I leave, I shall tell you what his character is without flattering you, so that you and your husband can correct it.'

During the two feast days, the old man kept little Nicolas with him all the time, winning his affection with sugar and chestnuts. He put him to the test in different ways to discover the child's character, and it was not difficult to fathom. On the second day, when all the family had withdrawn, old Ferlet said to his daughter and son-in-law: 'My children, you see me radiant with joy. I understand the child just like I understand his mother. Listen to me both of you. Nicolas is lively; he takes after you my girl, and after your mother. He is like you were as a child, and if you were a good daughter and if you are a good wife . . . Is she, son-in-law?'

'Excellent, and more than that, if it were possible, father.'

'He's a lively child, but he's artless. Like you, he can't tolerate being humiliated or dominated. And even at his age, he thinks himself as important as the king and has no intention of putting up with anything from other people, not even from you his own mother and father. I have tested him in every possible way, and tomorrow I will put him to the test in front of you. That is all I have to say this evening. Tomorrow at breakfast as I am about to leave, I will reveal the rest to you.'

Barbare threw her arms around her husband's neck and then around her father's knees, saying to the one: 'Ah, nothing but good can emanate from such a man as you, husband,' and to the other, 'you restore your daughter to joy and happiness, for they had almost gone completely because of the distress that this child caused me as he grew up.'

The next day at breakfast, old Ferlet called Nicolas who had just got out of bed. He ran to his grandfather.

'Nicolas, my son, I hear that you are dutiful and obedient to your father and to your mother, my daughter. And if you aren't, I shall punish you like the dog here, when he was learning to retrieve birds that had been shot.'

Nicolas scowled at him, and although he was a pretty child, he became ugly because of his anger and the blackness of his look. He turned his back without answering, but he broke his little horse and little cart, and threw his skittles and his ball onto the fire. His little clay figures were smashed to dust. Then he sat down with his back to them.

'Nicolas,' his grandfather said to him, 'I said what I did to test you. Do you really think that grandpa would treat you like a gun dog, after showing you so much kindness yesterday? Oh, I thought you had a sense of humour. Your father has, your mother has, but you haven't. Ho, ho, who do you take after then?'

Nicolas turned round. 'I'm not stupid like the gun dog.'

'No, but you don't have as much sense as I thought you had, otherwise you'd have taken it as a joke. It was said in jest. I love your mother, my daughter, too much not to love you with all my heart. Come here.'

The child didn't run, he hurled himself into his grandfather's arms, with tears in his eyes.

'That's not all. I want you to be friends with your mother, because she's been worried about you, very worried indeed.

For the more one loves one's child, the more worried one is when one thinks he's a bad boy. I told your father and your mother yesterday evening that you would be a good lad, that you loved them dearly, and that you were only a child and too spirited. They believed me and they'll both give you a kiss.'

Indeed, his mother stretched out her arms to him. But as he had to pass in front of his father, the child went first to him. He was shaken by the hand, which was his father's way of caressing him. Then looking at his mother, he said something beyond his years (he was eight): 'Kiss my sisters (he had two), but don't kiss me. Order me to do whatever you wish and I will obey you.'

'Just like his mother,' the old man said quietly. 'As a child she couldn't bear being kissed. She even spurned us. Nicolas, your father loves you, but if he were in danger, and let's suppose you had to put your hand in the fire to save him, would you do it? There, if you had to?'

'Yes, yes, grandpa.'

'And for me?'

'Yes, yes, grandpa.'

'And for your mother?'

'Even more so, grandpa.'

'We'll see if you are telling the truth, for your mother really needs a little help from you. If you love your mother, you must prove it.'

The child did not reply, but went straight to the fire-place, and whilst they were making signs to each other not suspecting what he was about to do, he put his hand in the fire. His mother noticed first. She let out a piercing cry, rushed to the child, and pulled him back, his hand already injured. She fainted. Taken by surprise, his father and grandfather thought only of coming to her aid.

'Wait, wait,' the little boy said, 'I'll burn the other one so as to revive her. This one's hurting too much.'

His grandfather had to leave his daughter and to hurl himself at the child. His mother came to her senses and her first gesture was to kiss her son's painful hand. Then she got up as quick as lightning and went to find some fresh butter, with which she covered it. She bandaged it and wanted to keep the child on her lap.

'Let me go, mother,' he said. 'You can be sure that you will soon be spared, because I'm suffering a lot.' And he laughed. 'I'm going to run around so that I don't feel it so much, unless you say I mustn't.'

'Oh my child!' his mother cried, 'my poor child, to whom I've been so unjust. My poor child!'

'Let us not judge children too soon,' old Ferlet then said, 'and before we do, let us try every means we can, and if one is not successful, then let us wait a little longer. There are men who are not mature at thirty or even thirty-five. If one judges them earlier, it is like eating an excellent fruit whilst it is still green and condemning the tree on that basis. With some men, and sometimes the greatest, one has to wait until they are tested in the fire of adversity, so to speak, before they reveal their goodness. But your son won't have to go to those limits. Goodbye son-in-law, goodbye daughter. Take care of your child's hand, and remember that he has a generous nature. Treat him as a man before his time, and you'll see what he'll grow into. He may even exceed your hopes.'

Barbare had six other children, the two daughters and four boys, which made Edme Rameau the father of fourteen children. She brought her daughters up with the greatest care, teaching them what she knew: thrift, cleanliness, and orderliness of course, respect for the first sex; inculcating in them from the beginning, by her own example and that of women whose behaviour was entirely the opposite, that the only way of achieving happiness in marriage was to be submissive to their husband, to cherish him, and to make him so contented that he would be obliged to recognise how much he needed his wife.

She was extremely fond of all her children, especially Nicolas and her daughter Barbare, who was the prettier of the two girls. But her two favourites were precisely the two to whom she showed the least indulgence. However, if they experienced any sorrow, ah, how her maternal heart shared it.

Never did a step-mother possess the virtues of this dubious role to such a high degree as Barbare Ferlet. Soon after her marriage, she became aware of her grown-up step-daughters' jealousy and of their attempts to turn their brothers against her. One of them, Edme-Nicolas, was a priest, but the respect in which he held his mother's memory made him unjust towards Barbare. He believed his sisters' calumnies. They even interpreted a wife's natural fondness for her husband in an unfavourable light, depicting it as the consequence of an inclination to lust. It must be said that the piety that these girls professed is a very dangerous thing. It poisons everything, and scoundrels are no worse in their way than pious women. The upright man, the upright woman are neither affectedly pious nor wicked, but bear out the admirable maxim of Confucius, 'It is better not to attain virtue than to exaggerate it.' Barbare suffered her step-daughters' injustice without a murmur. She never complained to her husband of the remarks which came to her notice. She married off the eldest as her own daughter and friend. The second wanted to go to Paris to stay with an aunt on her father's side. Barbare deprived herself on her account. She used up the small savings she'd made and in this way showed her preference over her own children. The seminarist received nothing but kindness from her. She urged her husband to allow the younger one to study, even though the boy's maternal grandfather was opposed to it. Furthermore, she saw to it that the other girls were set up, and worked for twelve years solely for them so that each would have a good trousseau. They repaid her with ingratitude, and yet to the end of her days she respected the priest just as she did her husband.

Her Nicolas had smallpox at twelve and became as ugly as he had been good-looking. When he recovered, his loving mother, who had watched over him for twenty nights in succession, seeing that he was sad about his ugliness, addressed him in the following manner, which would have outshone even a woman brought up in the town where they are so learned and so wise: 'What! a boy, nearly a man, thinks about his good looks like a woman. Ah, my son, what weakness, what childishness. You may be assured that your accidental ugliness will be an advantage not only to you, but also to the honest girl you will one day take as a wife. The purity of your blood will not suffer, and she will have a husband who is less foppish, less preoccupied with himself, and more admiring of her. For if good sense has taught me one thing, my son, it is that a husband and wife must admire each other if they are to

be happy. She must be amazed by her husband's qualities and
knowledge; he must be enchanted by his wife's charms. If the
wife is learned and the husband good-looking, there will be
no admiration, no happiness. Your father intends that you
should live in town. How unfortunate if you had kept your
effeminate good looks. They would have proved a snare for
you and for others a corrupting lure. I like you better, my son,
with that manly face, which won't attract the coquettes, but
which will never arouse aversion in a sensible, kind, and
sober-minded girl, which is what you need.'

When Nicolas reached sixteen, his mother noticed that the
young man had a lusty temperament. She was even more
pleased about his ugliness, and she gave him sound advice.
She filled his heart with honest feelings of love for one of his
cousins, a kind and innocent girl, as the daughters of honest
ploughmen are remote from the corruption of towns. This
was the only measure his mother took, persuaded as she was
that a virtuous love was the surest safeguard for his precocious
temperament. But having been placed in the town, the young
man found himself far from the watchful eye of his mother.
However, the sound principles which he had learnt from her
sustained him for a while. This is not his story. He fulfilled the
destiny predicted for him by his grandfather Ferlet.

Barbare never went back on her promise. She remained as
attentive as ever towards her husband; and she even went so
far as to send the servants out to meet him when he returned
home a little late at night, for fear that he might be attacked.
He tried to reassure her on his arrival; but she could never
control her anxiety, which her lively imagination exaggerated
beyond the bounds of reason.

This worthy wife and mother had her share of suffering in
her life. Her own children equalled in number those of the first
marriage, but they were reduced to three boys and two girls.
She lost two of her sons; one at the age of fifteen in Paris
where he was learning a trade, the other, who was of the
highest worth and most good-looking, at the age of seventeen
in Hanover where he was serving in the army. The former
was dearly loved by his father Rameau, who showed a special
fondness for him on account of his unaffected and touching
good-heartedness that revealed his true character. Moreover,

this good-heartedness reminded Edme Rameau of a great-uncle who had shown him much affection. He used to say, talking of this his second son, he's just like my dear uncle. He has his character. God has given him back to me in this child. One may judge from his observation how much he mourned his loss. Mme Rameau saw her husband's grief and shared it as a wife and mother. But at the death of their third son, of whom they had high expectations which he doubtless would have fulfilled, they experienced not a tender grief, as at the death of their second son, but despair, dejection, deep unhappiness. Their eldest son's true worth was not yet recognized, and the fourth and the youngest were still too small for their character to be known. Husband and wife were plunged into grief that was nearly fatal.

Edme Rameau had scarcely recovered from this terrible shock, when he suffered further distress, caused by his son Nicolas. This young man was given to violent passions. He had loved one of his first cousins until she got married, and this passion which had been guided and encouraged by his mother had had no harmful effect upon his behaviour. After this, he was placed in the town where he fell in love with a pretty vine-dresser, whereupon he was sent to the capital. There he was master of his own destiny, and, with his senses roused to fever pitch, he went astray. If he had not fallen in love . . . but he fell for an adventuress, a young English woman who perhaps lacked morals. He asked his father if he could marry her. Edme Rameau, who was well informed, refused. Carried away by his passion, the son provoked his father's anger, added to his suffering at the loss of the brother, and brought upon himself the most terrible threats. All these sorrows combined hastened perhaps the death of Edme Rameau.

Barbare Ferlet was widowed at the age of fifty, and she lived for another sixteen years during which she mourned the loss of her husband and wore her widow's weeds. It was this upright woman's conduct which imbued her sons with respect for womankind, especially Nicolas who always considered women as the image of divinity in the eyes of men. It is in the light of these remarks that one must judge the works he has published, which have wounded the feelings of certain

women. But if he has affirmed so strongly the necessity for
wives to be submissive to their husbands, it is because he is
convinced that this is the only way that they will achieve
happiness. His loving mother did not live to witness her son's
success, but she received her recompense in the respect of the
eldest son of the first marriage, who finally did her justice as
she deserved. This worthy woman had been happy until the
death of her husband. Sorrows assailed her thereafter; and the
grief caused by her daughter Barbare's marriage to a man who
was unsuitable led her to the grave: 'Ah, if I had my worthy
husband, my protector, my support, my daughter would not
have dared give me this heart-ache.' She died in the arms of
her dear son Nicolas, who sacrificed for her his passion for the
English woman. He did everything to save his mother. He did
not succeed and he weeps for her still.

Reader, one often talks of those one loves, one represents
them in different lights. Look at *My Father's Life*, at *Monsieur
Nicolas* when it appears. A certain M. Milran of Cherbourg
was astonished to find such variety in certain stories. He
dosen't know the human heart!

THE WORLD IN YOUR POCKET
some Pocket Classics from Alan Sutton

Good reading in a handy pocket size, attractively produced and priced, featuring the works of major writers generally not available elsewhere in paperback.

POCKET CLASSICS

W.N.P. BARBELLION – The Journal of a Disappointed Man
ARNOLD BENNETT – Elsie and the Child and Other Stories
Whom God Hath Joined – Helen with the High Hand
JOSEPH CONRAD – Within the Tides
DANIEL DEFOE – Captain Singleton
MRS GASKELL – The Manchester Marriage
My Lady Ludlow
THOMAS HARDY – Life's Little Ironies
JACK LONDON – The Star Rover
CAPTAIN MARRYAT – Peter Simple
THOMAS LOVE PEACOCK – Gryll Grange
HESTHER LYNCH PIOZZI – Anecdotes of Samuel Johnson
R. S. SURTEES – Ask Mamma
Mr Facey Romford's Hounds – Mr Sponge's Sporting Tour
WILLIAM THACKERAY
Samuel Titmarsh and the Great Hoggarty Diamond
ANTHONY TROLLOPE – The Bertrams
Lady Anna – An Old Man's Love – The Three Clerks
FANNY TROLLOPE – Domestic Manners
of the Americans

CONTINENTAL CLASSICS

HONORÉ DE BALZAC – A Passion in the Desert
RÉTIF DE LA BRETONNE – My Father's Life
ANTON CHEKHOV – The Black Monk and Other Stories
ALEXANDRE DUMAS – The Lady of the Camellias
IVAN TURGENEV – Smoke
EMILE ZOLA – The Fortune of the Rougons

TRAVEL CLASSICS

FREDERICK BURNABY – On Horseback Through
Asia Minor
HENRY SEEBOHM – The Birds of Siberia:
To the Petchora Valley – The Birds of Siberia: The Yenesei
ANTHONY TROLLOPE – The West Indies and the
Spanish Main
FANNY TROLLOPE – Paris and the Parisians

Available from all good bookshops. Complete catalogue from:
Alan Sutton Publishing, 30 Brunswick Road, Gloucester GL1 1JJ

HONORÉ DE BALZAC

A PASSION IN THE DESERT

The tales in this volume are among Balzac's best, ranging from the title story in which a panther conceives dog-like affection for a fugitive soldier, to the feelings of the French King's executioner in *An Episode of the Reign of Terror*. *The Conscript* is a memorable study of telepathy. Probably the best of all his short stories, *La Grande Bretèche* is a striking example of the workings of the romantic imagination in which the author turns the sinister aspect of an old fortress into a remarkable little drama.

The odd contradictions which beset a materialist with warm feelings make for a splendid study in *The Atheist's Mass*, set in Paris, whilst in the remaining three stories the reader is transported to Spain during the Peninsula War; a tiny peninsula in Brittany; and finally in *Facino Cane* we are introduced to a patrician of Venice with a tale to tell of treasures beyond compare.